At thirty-seven, Geeorge W. Cornell, Religion Editor of *The Associated Press,* is firmly established as one of the country's leading writers on religion. In 1954 he was cited for outstanding coverage of the field by the National Religious Publicity Council. Born in Oklahoma, Mr. Cornell studied journalism at the University of Oklahoma, and during World War II was an infantry lieutenant and officer in charge of the *Daily Pacifican,* published in the Southwest Pacific Theater. He now lives in New York City with his wife and daughter.

rb reconstruction of the Gospel ı sense, two inspiring books in an intimate portrayal of 24 of temporaries at those climactic ıen their lives were shaken by od. Here are the major figures; ıre others less familiar — the Woman, Pretonius, Joses, for example — all brought to vivid life. Second, in all and through all, is revealed with startling freshness the towering figure of Jesus Himself — the epic events of His sojourn on earth and His ultimate meaning for the world.

A detail from "Christ and the Rich Young Ruler" by
Heinrich Hofmann. Copyright New York Graphic Society.

THEY KNEW JESUS

THEY KNEW

JESUS

BY GEORGE W. CORNELL

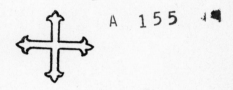

A 155

WILLIAM MORROW AND COMPANY · NEW YORK

1957

For
My Mother and Father
who also know Him

CONTENTS

CONTENTS

8

CONTENTS

FOREWORD

LL HISTORY is a mosaic of individuals, their weaknesses, their courage, their wisdom and their follies. These are the elements that shaped the days of Jesus of Nazareth on earth.

He developed his work within the framework of his contemporaries. Through them, he presented himself. Through them, he achieved his own purpose and destiny. And both his stature and his nature are most clearly seen through those who knew him.

These accounts, based on the Bible and historical sources, depict those men and women—friends and foes, intimates and strangers—who figured in the life that stands as an enduring standard of man's ideals, a tragic symbol of his waywardness, and also a beacon of his hopes. They were human beings, caught up in a dramatic venture that transcended their personal limitations. But they were the language that told the story.

THEY KNEW JESUS

1

MARY

"For unto us a child is born . . ."

LYING ON THE straw pallet, the young woman watched a beetle creep upward on the stone wall. In the pale lantern light, it moved slowly, taking very long, it seemed, to gain a finger's breadth. Mary smiled dreamily. Poor little beetle, you have to climb so far and so hard. But you will make it. All is well, blessedly well. Never had she known a stable could be so comforting.

Just outside the entrance, Joseph stood outlined against the wan night, a dark, steadfast sentry. From beyond came the faint singing of crickets. Mary breathed deeply and evenly. The intense sublimity of the moment pervaded her whole being.

Keep going, little beetle. You can do it. You clasp the hewn stone so determinedly, searching ahead with tiny legs. Do not be fearful. The shelter here is good and pleasant. Fear not . . . fear not. The Lord is nigh.

15

Mary murmured indistinctly, and then the melting bliss came back over her. She let her eyes rove about the stall. The lantern, sheathed in hare skin, cast a wavering, mellow glow. In the farther shadows, animals sighed and slept, the hobbled burros, the cattle tied by chains to iron rings in the wall. Mary always would cherish this quiet, secure place, its sturdy, soiled walls. None of this night would ever leave her.

She had been relieved beyond words when Joseph found a refuge, at last, after his unavailing entreaties at the inn. Good Joseph. He had not known how spent the journey from Nazareth to Bethlehem had left her. The stable had been as welcome as a palace.

And all the marveling days before. . . . Ever since the divine message had come that she would bear a son, not by man, but of God, her soul had magnified the Lord. He had chosen her—a lowly village girl—as his handmaiden. "Thou . . . art highly favoured . . . highly favoured." The words kept returning, soft and deep within her, like a reassuring embrace. ". . . the Lord is with thee . . ."

At first, she had been confused and troubled. But needlessly so. "Fear not, Mary: for thou hast found favour with God." She didn't understand it at once, but she could only say, God's will be done. So now the time had come, and she basked in the wonder of it. Yet, how mystifying still. That it should be she, poor, of no rank, of humble habit. . . . The Lord did shatter the pretensions of the proud and the great.

Press on, little beetle. Mary's fingers clasped the edges of the covering. The beetle strained upward, hugging the ridges of stone. Hold tight, gallant one. Your body sways so heavily on its frail legs. But you are gaining. Ever so surely.

Mary let her head lean to one side, and the rapture came over her, like warm surf. Every passing moment, every thing around, seemed highly precious. Lying there, wrapped in a woolen shawl, on the soft, fragrant bed of straw, she could feel at moments the very core of her life hurtling toward some poignant fulfillment, then dissolving into pure serenity. She was suffused with an unutterable peace and gratitude.

Nothing, nothing at all, remained of the agitation in which she had hastened to her cousin's house in the hill country after first learning she would bear a holy son. Elisabeth had understood at once. "Blessed art thou among women, and blessed is the fruit of thy womb." The elderly woman's voice quavered. ". . . mother of my Lord . . ."

Mary had stayed there three months, her feelings churning. Never had she talked so much, this young, quiet and thoughtful girl, but the magnitude of her secret had flooded over her. ". . . my spirit hath rejoiced in God my Saviour. . . . from henceforth all generations shall call me blessed. For he that is mighty hath done to me great things; and holy is his name. . . . He hath shewed strength with his arm . . . He hath put down the mighty from their seats, and exalted them of low degree. He hath filled the hungry with good things . . . in remembrance of his mercy." And Elisabeth had listened, with tender concern.

On Mary's return home, Joseph had been disturbed, but in time he also had understood. Though he was older than she, his joy had become as boundless as hers as the time neared. She had spent the days plainly—weaving, drying fruit, grinding grain—but with a bright treasure in her heart.

Now, in this soothing haven, with light flickering on the rafters and her good husband at call, she drifted at intervals in delicious reverie. Waves of happiness flowed over her like music, ebbing and swelling. She found herself gazing mistily at the beetle again. It had traversed two more stones and still struggled heroically. Do not give up, little beetle. There is not far to go.

The stable, the night, the world itself seemed to be expanding around her, and the lantern light was more alive. She felt as if she were floating, rising, until she almost touched the very heavens. Almost. . . .

Somewhere, as if far away, she heard a chain clink and knew that some animal on the other side of the stable had shifted position in the night, but it all seemed very distant, very far away. Then suddenly her eyes were open and she was staring directly across the room at a cow, placidly chewing, the eyes big and kind. Mary gazed at her fondly. The cow was so friendly, such a close companion.

Sweet night! Good stable! Dear creatures of God! Little beetle, you're almost to the upper ledge. Reach, reach up! Suspense, an excitement, was gathering in her, gathering slowly, increasing, gathering steadily and more swiftly.

She could not hear the crickets any more, but a stronger, greater rhapsody was ringing out through all the earth. Her eyes were closed. Her lips moved rapidly in prayer. Her heart filled until it seemed almost bursting. She felt lifted up, up, up in an infinite design, a part of the miracle of all creation, sharing a secret with God. And the stars raced by.

Then, all was still. The night was silent.

Joseph!

A newborn baby boy puckered up his face and let out his first cry.

Joseph already was beside her, and she was looking up at him, and crying a little bit herself, but smiling, too, and she saw he also was crying. It seemed so very foolish, because she could not be happier, and she doubted if he could be, either, but she looked at the baby, and burst out crying all over again.

Blessed Mary, Joseph kept saying. Praise God! He was saying first one and then the other.

She took some swaddling cloth they had brought, and wrapped the baby, and laid him in the clay manger. Joseph had removed the fodder and put in some straw to make it soft, and after the baby was there, Joseph kept moving about, not doing very much, but just hovering, as if he should do something but did not know what to do; and every so often he would stop and look at the baby, blinking his eyes, and then he would start moving about again, mumbling and breathing very hard, and stopping to look first at her and then the baby in a bewildered way.

Mary smiled at her husband, shaking her head, but the tears kept coming, and she couldn't help it.

She must not have noticed for a long time that the beetle had reached the high ledge.

"And there were in the same country shepherds abiding in the field, keeping watch over their flock by night. And, lo, the angel of the Lord came upon them, and the glory of the Lord shone round about them: and they were sore afraid.

"And the angel said unto them, Fear not: for, behold, I bring you good tidings of great joy, which shall be to all people. For unto you is born this day in the city of David a Saviour, which is Christ the Lord.

"And this shall be a sign unto you; Ye shall find the babe wrapped in swaddling clothes, lying in a manger.

"And suddenly there was with the angel a multitude of the heavenly host praising God, and saying, Glory to God in the highest, and on earth peace, good will toward men."

2

SIMEON

"Then took he him up in his arms, and blessed God . . ."

ONCE AGAIN, as he had on so many days before, Simeon made his way toward the Temple. On this morning, as on so many mornings before, he hearkened to a ringing hope. It called him, guided him, held him fast. It would not let him go. He strode along, his eyes lit with an old yearning, and words of the ancients whispered in his ears, "Behold, the Lord God will come with a strong hand . . . And he will lift up an ensign to the nations from far . . ."

Simeon's jaw thrust forward, and he spread his arms, savoring the new day. Dew still shimmered on the lime-whitened façades of the city, and he tasted the salt of promise in the air. This might be the season, the month, the very hour! Had it not, indeed, been revealed to him that he would live to see the Lord's child? Many had discounted his expectations with a shrug, but he had not been dissuaded. Today, belief coursed through him as strong as desire.

The elderly rabbi paused beside a pool, with a pillared arcade surrounding it, and prayed silently. The old prophecies of Isaiah glowed in him, fresh and bright as the sun on the waters of the pool: ". . . and his name shall be called Wonderful, Counsellor, The mighty God, The everlasting . . . Prince of Peace. Of the increase of his government and peace there shall be no end . . ."

He went on then, the black tallith on his head flowing waist-length behind him. Jerusalem stirred and awakened as he moved through the streets. Smiths blew at their coals. Dyers, cloth merchants, sandal makers and perfume mixers set up their wares in their open shops. Dealers in sour wine clashed their copper dishes to lure buyers. The smell of baking loaves came from the ovens.

Always on his passage through the city, Simeon grieved at the corroding forces that wasted the nation, scattered her people and riddled the city with pagan aliens, their crude sports, their prostitutes and debased idolatry. Roman soldiers, Greeks in short tunics, and painted, bespangled women mingled with Israel's threadbare poor, the bondslaves in their aprons and felt caps, the donkey drivers, and aristocrats in their blue-striped robes.

For seven centuries, Israel had felt the lash of conquerors—Assyrian, Egyptian, Macedonian, Persian, Babylonian, Roman—and hundreds of thousands of her people had been slain, hauled off into slavery or dispersed to the four winds. Rome's truckling tyrant, Herod the Great, now sat on the throne, and the world's orgiastic cults of Cybelle, Dionysus, Diana and Astarte beat against Judaism's small, battered bastion of faith in the one true God.

Along the street snake charmers untied their baskets, soothsayers beckoned, and sellers of elixirs and magic potions set up their stands.

Simeon realized that all the outward signs contradicted his belief that an exalted leader would emerge above the ruin, that God's emissary soon would come. But the certainty burned in him. Hope refuted reason. Unconvinced by evidences, he hoped on, looking for the never seen, knowing that sometimes out of deepest paradox arose the clearest reason, and from the darkest night, the brightest dawn.

Ahead of him, sparkling on Mount Zion like a snow-white diadem, stood the Temple, its marble arches and towers vaulting into the sun. "Behold . . . the Lord, whom ye seek, shall suddenly come to his temple . . . And he shall sit as a refiner and purifier . . ."

Simeon's spirits quickened, and his deep-lined, bearded face mellowed in thanksgiving as he gazed once again on the familiar sight. The wisdom of the prophet Malachi seemed to spring from the air of this very moment. No matter how many people disparaged Simeon's claim that he would see the Lord's advent, he himself had no doubt. The Lord would come! He would come suddenly to the Temple!

Bending against the incline, he moved on up the stone street.

Despite the pompous priests and their cupidity, the Temple alone survived as the chief emblem of a rich history, a holy ideal. Destroyed repeatedly by invaders, it always rose again, symbol of imperishable truths, of the stubborn heroes of Israel. The blood of Simeon blended with that noble stream, with the great judges and teachers, and he clung relentlessly to the old, high aspirations.

He climbed the ramp to the royal portico where he often taught. It was a long, majestic porch, with four rows of monolithic marble columns crowned by Corinthian capitals, 162 of them in all. They formed three aisles, covered by a ceiling of carved cedar—one of four cloisters stretching 4,260 feet around the Temple walls. He took his place there on a raised stone seat, waiting for his students to gather. There were not many of them any more. His own vision had scant acceptance. They came gradually, the older ones sitting at his feet, the younger ones standing behind them.

As he often did, he lectured today on the prophets: the great Isaiah of seven hundred years ago, who had fought against the injustices of priests and rulers only to be called disloyal; the vigorous, rural prophet, Micah, of about the same time; the priestly Malachi of five hundred years ago; the gentle, but rapier-tongued Jeremiah, who had endured prisons and floggings for his piercing wisdom 600 years ago; Amos, Joel, Ezekiel, Zechariah and Daniel. All were discerning men, driven by an inner mandate to be spokesmen for the Lord.

All the while Simeon spoke, their predictions of a coming great redeemer filled his thoughts. It was astonishing how many aspects they foresaw in him. They said he would be lowly, but also a light that would draw even pagan Gentiles from far and near to its brilliance. He would be a man of sorrows ere his glory could be known.

Ezekiel said he would be like a shepherd feeding his flocks. Many said he would be of the line of David. As recorded by Jeremiah's scribe, Baruch, the Lord would ". . . raise unto David a righteous Branch . . ." to ". . . make a new covenant . . ." to free people of their sin. Micah gave him a humble birthplace: "But thou, Bethlehem . . . though thou be little among the thousands of Judah, yet out of thee shall he come forth . . . whose goings forth have been from of old, from everlasting." Daniel, in his vision, perceived that the chosen one would be like a man, but would be given ". . . an everlasting dominion, which shall not pass away . . ." He would be, Isaiah said, ". . . as an hiding place from the wind, and a covert from the tempest . . . And an highway shall be there, and a way . . . the redeemed shall walk there . . . the ransomed of the Lord . . ."

Simeon, swept by feelings he could not fathom, finished his discourse earlier than usual, dismissed the group, and strolled off along the cloisters. He stroked his gray beard thoughtfully.

To the east side of the Temple, called Solomon's porch, the usual swarm of pitiful creatures lay outside on the ground, the blind, the sick and lame with shrunken bodies and twisted limbs. Simeon distributed what money he had with him, and walked away. How urgently the Lord's elect was needed amidst these miseries!

He went through a huge gold-plated gate into the outer court, and the bleating of lambs and the flapping of caged pigeons assailed his ears. Voices swirled in noisy bartering. Hawkers shouted; money-changers rattled their plates to attract people to their tables, and the smell of offal rose from the animal stalls. All the din and clutter seemed unfitting at the Temple, but the priests defended it as necessary. Worshipers had to have unblemished animals for sacrifice, and it was difficult to bring them long distances. The money-changers, for a fee, provided a convenience for converting other monies into the shekel or half-shekel required for the Temple corban.

As Simeon traversed the open court, amid the clamor, he heard dimly a baby's cry. It tugged at him oddly, almost stopping him, but he walked on, climbing the steps to a low stone balustrade enclosing those inner portions of the Temple which only Jews could enter. Tablets in Greek, Hebrew and Latin hung along the parapet, barring foreigners on pain of death. Temple guards, naked to the waist and with their tablets of authority hanging on their chests beneath plaited beards, patrolled the area, carrying thonged whips.

As Simeon started through the inner gate, he again hesitated. An overpowering intuition, not unlike that which had made him sure he would see God's ambassador, halted him there on the raised terrace. A deep, inner counseling rushed through him like a river breaking its banks.

He turned about, striving to calm his emotions, knowing no recognizable reason for them, other than his general mood of expectancy on this day. And that baby's muted plaint. . . . It is patience, he reminded himself, constant, confident patience that will see God's word fulfilled. He must not be carried away by his own meditations.

Involuntarily his gaze roved over the outer court. He shaded his eyes from the sun, still baffled by his own motives. The place was becoming more crowded as the day wore on. Rich and poor from towns and fields were coming to pay their tithes and make their gifts.

As he studied the scene, his attention fell on a couple with an infant. His heart leaped, and an ineffable delight swelled in him. He tried to tell himself that it was only because the couple looked upright, happy and devoted, and because he found pleasure in wholesome beauty, but he knew that a weightier cause might be responsible for the promptings within him. Plainly the couple were country folk of meager means, the man older than the woman. She wore a freshly washed and sunned palla and a wrap-around *caniph* over her head; she carried the child in a woven cloth of soft goat hair. The man was a steady-looking workman, with roughened hands and a brown, kindly face. He held a closed basket, presumably with birds in it for sacrifice when they presented the child to the Lord. Both appeared in festive spirits as they stared about at the bustle of the great city and the Temple. The young mother had a radiant innocence and purity about her.

"Behold, a virgin shall conceive, and bear a son . . ." The words of Isaiah flashed through Simeon's mind. ". . . with righteousness shall he judge the poor . . . with equity for the meek of the earth . . ."

The rural family came up the steps and walked by Simeon, their heads bowing slightly to the rabbi. With difficulty, he held back the intuitive knowledge bursting within him.

He hurried out to the stall of pigeons and turtledoves to make inquiries. The couple, he learned, were Joseph and Mary, both of the line of David, and the child had been born in Bethlehem, where they now lived—all as the prophecies had foretold. The child, when circumcised at the age of eight days, had been named "Yeshua," or Jesus, which meant the "Salvation of God." Simeon's assurance soared. The infant was the very one about whom the shepherds had told their tale of heavenly signs some weeks ago—a tale which few had given credence, the synagogue rulers saying it was a reckless tale, fit for humor, or entertaining children.

Simeon rushed back into the Court of Women (where women as well as men were permitted) and his eyes sought out the Bethlehem couple. He stood observing them, filled with a sense of ultimate happiness, of a long journey's end.

Inside the court, the clink of coins made a steady tinkling sound as people dropped offerings into the large trumpet-shaped containers that stood near thirteen of the pillars of the colonnade. White-robed Levites were just removing their instruments from beneath the semicircular stairway, in preparation for the midmorning Shema. Simeon's gaze stayed on the visiting couple as they watched the activities. He did not want to interrupt them until they had concluded their duties.

The Levitical choir gathered on the broad, looping stairs that led to the next inner court of Israel, and began the chanting of psalms of praise, interspersed with the soaring music of silver trumpets. Pilgrims pressed their faces to the tiled floor in prayer.

To Simeon, the music today seemed to come down from the very firmament, like the singing of angels, and the silver voice of Isaiah made melody in his soul. "For unto us a child is born, unto us a son is given . . . Arise, shine; for thy light is come, and the glory of the Lord is risen upon thee. . . . Lift up thine eyes . . . and see . . ."

Simeon got up from the floor and straightened his tallith, his glad eyes dwelling on the little family across the court. They doubtlessly had come to dedicate the child at the age of forty days.

Although a lamb for a burnt offering and a turtledove or young pigeon for a sin offering were the customary lawful sacrifices for a newborn son, the poor were permitted to offer instead only two birds. Inside the Court of Israel (which admitted only men) Simeon clasped his hands reverently, watching as Joseph arranged for the offering of the poor for the child Jesus. Joseph knelt outside the spiked fence, separating the Court of Israel from the raised, inner Court of Priests, with its high, pyramid-shaped stone altar, a ramp circling to the four horns at the top. Over to one side were the rings, hooks and tables for suspending, slaughtering and flaying the animals.

Psalms were spoken, and cymbals and harps played, as Joseph's small sacrifice was made.

He moved to another place, and paid the Temple tax for a first-born son, redeeming him for five shekels ($3.60), as was the law. He returned to the adjoining court, where Mary awaited him. They stood there, wreathed in smiles as they looked at the child. Jesus belonged to the Lord.

Simeon approached them, knowing that at last his dream had come to pass, his belief had become reality, and the consolation of Israel for which he had looked steadfastly had arrived this day. He addressed the couple tenderly and asked if he might hold the child in his arms. Mary handed him the baby Jesus. The old rabbi, his heart expanding in gratitude, a balm of peace in his soul, murmured praises of God as he lifted the wrap and looked down on the boy's face. He sighed contentedly, his lifelong wish achieved, the promise God had made to him kept.

"Lord," he said fervently, "now lettest thou thy servant depart in peace, according to thy word: for mine eyes have seen thy salvation, which thou hast prepared before the face of all people; a light to lighten the Gentiles, and the glory of thy people Israel."

His eyes misted, gazing at the child. Then he placed the infant back in the mother's arms, and looking on her guileless, young face, he thought of the sorrowful road that the sages of old foresaw for her child. She should be prepared; she should know what her son must endure for the sake of the people.

"Behold," he told her gently, "this child is set for the fall and rising again of many in Israel; and for a sign which shall be spoken against." Already they ignored, and disbelieved. He added, "Yea, a sword shall pierce through thy own soul also, that the thoughts of many hearts may be revealed."

The couple looked momentarily troubled, then glanced at the baby, proud and happy again. Simeon blessed them both, and they started on their way.

But then an ancient widow, a prophetess named Anna

of more than one hundred years of age who spent days and nights fasting and praying in the Temple, approached them and looked on the infant. She, too, was deeply moved, and her withered mouth began to speak excitedly, declaring that the boy was he who would bring redemption. She began hobbling about the court, telling it to all who would listen. Few would.

Simeon knew that. But the time would come. He watched the couple go, out through the ornamented gates, across the tumultuous court away from the Temple, in their spotless homespuns, carrying the little boy, disappearing into the distance.

He looked up to the shining peaks of the Temple, and to the heavens beyond. God's Son was not within the deep, inner sanctuary of this Temple, behind the heavy, bejeweled veil of the Holy of Holies, but out there on the dusty road to Bethlehem.

These things the old rabbi knew because he had believed. He had believed when there was no logic in believing. He had worn faith, woven of conviction, and it had lasted to his goal. He had kept alive a dream when others called it illusion. He had carried the torch of hope when no light shone, and in the winter of the world found springtime.

3

HEROD THE GREAT

*"Go and search diligently for the young child . . .
that I may come and worship him also."*

THE BLACK PAIN struck in his stomach
and spread achingly through his limbs.
Herod moaned. He clawed at the girdle
around his waist to loosen it. His face
ashen, he bawled at the waiting tribune:

"Destroy them, I say! All of them! Assemble your
men—take a whole cohort. Put the blade to every male
under two in that wormy city and for ten furlongs around!
Get on with it! Begone!"

The officer stepped back three paces, pivoted and
hurried out through the brocaded curtains, boots clicking
across the marble floor. The sound faded, died. Herod,
the ulcers cramping his belly and vitiating his flesh, threw
himself on a couch.

"Mariamne, oh, Mariamne. . . ." His lips moved,
whimpering, and he could smell his own foul breath.

Faces, ghostly faces—hers and many others—swam in his mind, the loved, the hated and the feared whom he had slain. The fools, the knaves, the turncoats, my sons, my wife! There seemed to be no end to the treachery. He couldn't escape it. The more plots he crushed, the more heads he lopped, the more the perfidy loomed around him. It reproduced and spread, gathering like vultures over a battleground. The very fiends of Hades rose to menace him. And now, this new hushed-up defiance.

Herod pressed a hand to his back, trying to relieve the pain in his abdomen.

The villainous peasants! The superstitious Jews, whispering about a new kingdom, a "God-king" born in Bethlehem. It was outright treason. Nothing else. A threat to his crown, an insult to the Roman Empire. These stubborn villagers could be as dangerous as the preened and perfumed traitors. They would get the same treatment. They would see how potent their suckling prince compared to Herod's sword.

He rolled over, staring blankly at the engraved cedar ceiling. "Oh, Mariamne. . . ." Did death remain his only consort? That hideous visage. It stalked about this palace, stealing into these very chambers, bending over this very couch.

Herod lunged heavily to his feet and stood there, swaying weakly. He bellowed to a porter for ewe's milk. As the fellow came running, Herod eyed him warily, watching for any movement of the hand under the loose chiton, any glint of metal. He brushed aside the proffered cup, took instead the jug and gulped down huge mouthfuls.

He paused, gasping, and waved the slave aside. A cluster of attendants and physicians began moving in toward him, with oily voices. "Might we aid thee, sire?" Herod roared at them and they fell back.

He placed the half-emptied jug on a stand beside the couch and sat down again, waiting for the soothing moisture to quiet the devils in his vitals. Gradually the sharpness eased a little, but his body felt heavy and flaccid.

He knew he was not the man he once had been, not by any measure. But he didn't need to lean on the arm of parasites. He was Herod. Herod the Great! His court didn't seem to realize it any more. They fawned about him as if he were some helpless idiot. By the gods, he'd tell them when he wanted them! They didn't have to brace up Herod! He had outdone the best of them in his time. He'd been a brilliant general in the field, a fearless hunter, a flawless marksman. Why, he once had caught forty wild beasts in a single day. These cooing doves! They didn't know mightiness when they saw it.

Herod sat there on the couch, rocking slightly, his eyes staring. He was sixty-nine. His wrinkled face had a flabby quality as if infused with too much fluid. The skin lay in folds about his neck. He suffered from ulcers, dropsy and fevers.

For forty-three years now, he had ruled Judea with the sanction of his Roman overlords, shrewdly shifting his allegiance from Julius Caesar to Mark Antony to Augustus as the tides of power changed, winning favor with each, treading cleverly amid the subtle intrigues and assassinations of Rome. He had seized the province in a splurge of carnage and stratagems, poisoning the Jewish leader, Malichus, and executing forty-five sympathizers in the Jewish governing council, the Sanhedrin. After the Senate in Rome had made him king of the province, he returned to smash new rebellions with the help of Roman troops, beheading the high priest Antigonus, jealously guarding his throne with the bloodshed that eventually had engulfed his own household. He could trust no one.

Suspicion infested his days, and lurking conspiracy his nights. He had even had to sacrifice Mariamne. . . . For what? The memory singed like fire.

Nothing was much good any more, he thought. Life had lost its color and shape and reason. But he couldn't give up. He had fought his way through too much guile and gore to give up now. He had gone too far not to keep going. It didn't matter why. He would smash any subverter, be he friend, priest, crafty politician or some nameless urchin in Bethlehem. A shudder went through him. His troops would be done with that business by nightfall, and be back with a full report.

Herod got to his feet again, and beckoned to his dresser to help him don the protective plates he hung over his chest and back of late whenever he ventured out of his private chambers. Then he pulled on his purple robe with the gold embroidery over the shoulders, and moved feebly out through the archway.

His four inner guards and a retinue of slaves followed him automatically. He went down the corridor and out on a balcony overlooking the sweeping esplanade with its wide, smooth pavement sloping up to the two wings of the palace. Carefully, the soreness still in his body, he sat down in an upholstered chair and dragged his feet up on a stool. He tried to inhale deeply to draw some vitality from the outdoor air, but the strain hurt his insides. He breathed shallowly through his mouth.

Those high-browed wizards from the distant East had incited this new undercover kingmaking! So they had seen it in the stars, had they? And traveled for months to hail this new inheritor of the earth!

He should have arrested them on the spot when they came through Jerusalem a week ago, arousing the whole city, explaining their abstruse calculations, carrying their gifts and planning to bend the knee to this mysterious heir. But he had thought he could lure them to bring him detailed information by pretending that he, too, would honor the infant. Instead, they had left the country by another route without telling him the child's identity. The close-lipped villagers wouldn't talk. All his spies had learned nothing. So the lot of them would pay.

Herod spat into a container placed at his side.

Well, it would just mean fewer mouths for the poor to feed. The Greeks who had settled here took care of these matters on their own. They just laid the newborn out to die if they didn't seem worth keeping, especially females. But the stiff-necked Jews didn't take to infanticide.

There was no pleasing them, anyway. He had sought strenuously to do so, at times. He had rid the land of brigands. He had dipped into the royal purse to distribute 800,000 measures of corn in famine, and clothed whole villages. He had built great monuments, forts, shrines, theaters, and a harbor at his new city, Caesarea, where none ever existed before. He had tried to fashion and beautify this laggard land with games, gymnasiums and the gaiety of Greece and his Roman liege. He prided himself on his buildings. He liked to see them rise in imposing grandeur, at his bidding.

But what did it avail him? More betrayals! Herod began mumbling to himself, uneasily. Some of these Bethlehem families might try to flee the town, or conceal their young as the ancient Jews did Moses. He should have instructed the tribune on this. "A messenger," he muttered. Then he shouted, "A messenger!"

A runner was hustled out to him, and a scribe. Herod dictated his further orders. "Barricade all roads while dispatching the nurslings of Bethlehem. Search every house. Search cisterns, brush and caves. Let none elude the king's wrath. By command of Herod." The scribe handed him the signet and he stamped it on the message with shaking hands. The runner set off.

Herod leaned back in the chair, half-closing his eyes. He should have included those points in his original orders. It might be too late. Not one below the age of two must escape. The Eastern sages had reported they had been almost a year journeying here after the heavenly signs appeared. The child could not be above two.

Perhaps he should have sent troops to pursue the departing philosophers and their camel train. The foreign interlopers, flouting his authority, sowing sedition! But he could not think of everything. His mind did not function as clearly as it once did. The duties and dangers crowded on him, mingling with the past until sometimes he could not separate the one from the other.

He realized suddenly that a porter stood before him and he jerked his head erect. "Speak! Speak! What say you?" The porter said nervously that the king's sister would have audience with him. "What? Very well. Let it be so. Send her!"

The porter left. Herod leaned back again. Women! Never trust them. Not even his own beguiling, much-married sister, Salome. None of them. Not even Mariamne? His mouth began to twitch, and he clapped a hand to his face to still it. But the facts remained. Women had schemed and preyed on him. Ten wives he'd had. All leeches. All but one. And he had sent her to death. "Oh, Mariamne, my beloved."

It had been partly a political gesture when he married her. She had been a princess of the Jews' royal Hasmonean line, and this gave his crown more native legitimacy. But the marriage became much more than that to him. She became his only heart, his refreshment, his resting place from the duplicity and the violence. But it couldn't stay that way. Mistrust, like a deep-rooted vine, had kept growing through Herod's castle.

Herod picked up the jug of milk placed beside him and poured down more of it to assuage the burning in his stomach and slake the liquid-consuming dropsy.

Mariamne hadn't been to blame. He knew that now. But other women had. Even at the start, a woman had

tried to wreck his newly bestowed kingdom. He had out-
foxed her.

Herod held the jug in his lap, and grinned wanly
through wet, blue lips.

Yes, he had been too shrewd for the wiles of greedy,
voluptuous Cleopatra. She had tried to entice him to her
bed to arouse the vengeance of Antony, ruler of Rome's
eastern domain, who carried on his adulteries with her in
Alexandria. She was scheming to annex Judea to her
Egyptian realm. Herod had rejected her blandishments.
He had kept his wits, kept Antony's favor and kept his
kingdom, even though she had stolen part of his southern
coastal lands for a time. He had his revenge, though, when
Augustus, the empire's ruler in Rome, made war on Antony, driving him and his mistress to suicide. As emperor,
Augustus had even returned to Herod the rich lands of
palms and balsam Antony had given to Cleopatra.

It hadn't stopped there, though. Not at all. Cleopatra
had managed to turn Mariamne's mother against him, ignit-
ing new plots among the Hasmoneans. He had had to
execute Mariamne's mother, her brother, her father, various other Jewish nobles, and finally, her love turned to
bitterness, Mariamne herself.

Herod took another swig of milk and tossed the
empty jug to the floor, shattering it. He wondered vaguely
what Salome wanted, and wished she would appear and
have done with it. Doubtlessly she was bedecking herself
before she emerged. Herod wiped his chin with a nerve-
less hand.

His gaze drifted out over the city, standing high above

the surrounding country, with its terraces and flat-roofed, whitewashed houses spilling down into the lower city, the towers and turrets and the great Temple with its alabaster spires. He had built that Temple, with eleven thousand slaves and priestly Levites. They had labored eight years to complete the main structure. Decorators still were adorning it with precious stones. But he resented the place. It represented nothing to him but unknown hostile forces.

More rewarding to him had been the shrines to Zeus and Diana he had built in other cities. That pleased the Romans. So did the treasure he had stripped from old King David's grave and given Rome, and his other tribute —money and monuments.

He could see, beyond the city's walls, the huge amphitheater he had built where he had introduced gladiatorial bouts, with up to 2,500 beasts slain in one entertainment. The Jews gave him no glory for it, though. It was true that some younger ones, along with Greeks and other Gentiles, joined in his projects. Most Jews despised him, however, scowling at the imported customs, the sports, the elaborate baths and theaters for music and nude dancing. They prattled against him, refusing to worship the Caesars, obsessed about their one God, spreading resistance. Even in his expenditures on the new Temple, they found cause for disruption. When he had the golden Roman eagles affixed to the east Temple gate, pious Jewish leaders tore them down, denouncing them as unholy, starting an uproar. He had had forty of them imprisoned in the hippodrome, where they languished now.

This new Bethlehem offense could cause untold consequences if it weren't dealt with forcefully.

Herod's eyes fixed on the tall, graceful Tower of Mariamne he had erected in her memory. His vision wavered and blurred. The tower seemed to divide and become several towers, and Mariamne appeared among them, moving in and out among them, in bloody clothes. . . .

Salome had come out on the balcony. Herod started. He looked up at her sullenly. She wore a flaming red gown and headdress, a golden chain about her neck. "I am told," she said, "that the king's eyes and ears have further knowledge of the conspiracy of Alexander and Aristobulus."

Herod's hands caught the sides of the chair, pulling himself forward. "What is it? What other knowledge could there be? What new knowledge?"

Not long ago, he had had Alexander and Aristobulus, his two sons by Mariamne, strangled. It had shaken him badly. But evidence of their plotting, as Hasmoneans, had been brought to him by Antipater, his son by another wife, and Salome herself. He had been compelled to kill them. He had to preserve his throne. That was all he had left. That and his ugly companion, death. "Speak, sister! Speak!"

She smiled at him ambiguously, her eyes ringed with cosmetics, the scent of thyme coming from her oil-rubbed body. "I know not its nature," she said. "Only that it is afoot, and I would prepare you."

He demanded that she tell more, but she insisted she knew no more. She was a cunning one, often hearing court gossip and the workings of his informers before he did. Raging, he ordered her out of his sight. He tottered as he got up, his blood vile, cankers in his joints, the dropsy making his thirst unslakable, the ulcers curling ropes of pain through his middle. He walked shakily back to his inner chambers, ordering his meal of gruel and more liquids. Afterward, his physicians administered nepenthe to enable him to rest.

That night, his military commander returned to report that the massacre in Bethlehem had been carried out, but that it was claimed at least one family had fled the city the night before. Convulsions shook Herod, and he could not make them stop.

A few days later, Salome's predictions materialized shatteringly. He learned that his son, Antipater, had fabricated the entire evidence against his half-brothers, Mariamne's sons, whom Herod had killed—though they were as innocent as she had been. In a frothing rage, he condemned Antipater to die. The fevers inflamed his brain, and the soreness coursed through his watery flesh. "Let it be a lesson!" he screamed. "Let death teach the liar and avenge my sons and Mariamne. Death to him! Death!" He also ordered the forty Jewish nobles who had torn down the eagles burned alive. "Death! Death!"

Herod went staggering through the halls of his mighty castle, screaming and gorging himself with liquid from the jug he carried in his hand. "Mariamne! Mariamne!" He shambled through the long, echoing corridors, through the huge empty dining hall with its one hundred couches, his eyes wild, his mouth contorted, screaming.

"Mariamne! Mariamne!" He tottered across the wide courtyard with its tall columns standing in their majesty, his brain on fire, his voice hoarse and pleading. "Mariamne. . . ." He tried to slay himself, but attendants stopped him.

Five days later, he died in agony, reputedly insane, and was buried on Frank Mountain south of Bethlehem. "A man he was of great barbarity to all men equally," wrote the ancient historian, Flavius Josephus. "He stole the throne like a fox, ruled like a tiger and died like a dog."

It was the end of a potentially great man, a clever, energetic man, who once never missed with javelin or arrow, who impressed Rome, who indulged in huge charities, but in whom evil bore its inevitable fruits. He killed his one good mate and his own sons, and left many Rachels weeping for their sons, but could not stay the Son of man.

Distrust, brutality and suspicion destroyed the only thing he ever loved, but could not destroy love itself, even in him. By debasing it, he died as he lived—afraid. And Jesus then was nearly two.

4

JOSEPH

*". . . he took the young child and his mother by night,
and departed into Egypt . . ."*

WALK SLOWLY NOW. *Think calmly,
Joseph. The town is quiet, but all the
night is filled with admonitions, with
murmurings and unseen storms—nebu-
lous things like finespun nets across a woodland trail,
brushing your face in the darkness.*

He stopped on the outskirts of Bethlehem, and stood
peering southward toward the black knobs of the hills.
He did not know. He could not be sure. But there could
be actual danger to the child. Uncommon things had come
to pass, and this might be another.

*Plan carefully, Joseph. The night is dark, and eyes
look out from every cryptic place. It is a hard decision.
All the apprehensions may be false. Yet they may be real.
And if they are, what can one lone man, an unknown,
landless carpenter, do against the might of kings? But
still . . . Oh God, it cannot be!*

Joseph, his arms bent at his sides, clenched his big, callused hands before him, glaring defiantly into the night. The sinews of his back, stooped from bending at his bench, stood out in ridges beneath his thin robe.

They shall not harm that boy! No man, neither infidel nor minion of the king, shall touch a hair of him!

For some moments he stood there, his paternally protective instincts thrashing like a gale among trees. Then he calmed himself, forcing his mind to consider, to be still and try to know. He must not let fanciful alarms shake their placid house. But if, in truth, a shadow fell across the child, if slings were cast against him in high places, then he must find the means to meet them. *The charge is yours, Joseph, is in your hands, the keeping of a life.*

Far to the south stretched the hills of Beersheba; beyond them, the desert . . . and Egypt. It would be a bitter road, a far and lonesome road, for Mary, for the baby, for all of them.

". . . O God . . ." his heart cried with the Psalmist. "What time I am afraid, I will trust in thee. . . . wilt not thou deliver my feet from falling . . . ?"

He turned back toward their house in Bethlehem, his heavy tread crunching against the stones and sticks.

For more than a year, they had lived in peace in Bethlehem, ever since the birth of Jesus. Then the Magi from the East had come, bringing precious gifts and worshiping the child, all of it a wonder to behold. But they had also voiced premonitions about the king, Herod the Great, saying they would not tell him, as he had asked, just where the child could be found, but would return to their own lands another way.

So now the vague threat hung over the child, and Joseph searched his duty.

Walk slowly, Joseph. To home and sleep. Search the forest of dreams, the valleys of the soul, whence many times you've drawn decision.

And so, it came, in his sleep, out of the depths of his concern and reverence, an inner voice saying: "Arise, and take the young child and his mother, and flee into Egypt . . . for Herod will seek the young child to destroy him."

In the middle of the night, Joseph arose from his bed of rushes. He awakened Mary and in quick, hushed tones told her they must go. Pack only what can be carried in haste, he said. He lit a lamp, and then hurried out to bring the burro from the field.

He loaded the animal in the dark, his hands skilled to balance and touch. He distributed utensils and his essential tools evenly on either side, and folded a tent on top for a seat, girding the load with two straps. The child was cradled in a sack slung at the burro's side. Then Joseph lifted Mary to the top of the level pack. He shouldered a sack of barley bread, cheese, dried fish and cucumbers, and a goatskin of water, and they started off. They said not a word as he led the burro through the sleeping town, and out into the hills.

Southward they traveled, avoiding the roads or hiding by day, moving mostly at night, watchful against pursuit. They circled towns, where soldiers might be posted, keeping much to remote trails and using the main roads only under cover of darkness. They traveled in haste, fighting off fatigue. They passed by Hebron and into the lonely stretches of Beersheba. On they went, and sometimes Joseph sat the burro to rest while Mary walked. Their supply of bread hardened, their cheese and fish ran out. They ate shriveled cucumbers and the bread, while the burro grazed on thistles and briars. They pressed on, and the child thrived, for he would remain a nursling until the age of two.

As the distance increased, they traveled by daylight, mingling with wayfarers, tenting at night, resting under a sycamore tree. They passed beyond the borders of Daroma and into the deserts, with no bush or tree for shade, where the wind heaved the sand into strange shapes and abutments and castles and caves. And Mary sat the donkey, shielding the child's eyes from the dust and the smiting sun. As the days ended, the flaming sunsets seemed to send their fire licking along the very sand. And then night closed down in sudden blackness. Chill crept in, and cold, and Joseph gave his cloak to wrap around the child.

This flight was not the first occasion that a troubled decision of Joseph's had protected the child. Once—it seemed long ago now—he had faced another painful crossroads. It had been in Nazareth, after his betrothal to Mary had been arranged.

That night, too, he had walked in darkness. . . .

It was as if the roots of his life had been torn away. Gladness turned into gall, and sorrow bent his shoulders and burned his bones as on a hearth. He did not know which way to turn, or what to do.

How tenderly he had cherished his betrothed, his Mary! Her pledge to him, at his greater age, had been like a healing touch, like a day star risen in his soul. Their betrothal vows had been like a marriage, sealed in full ceremony, and the betrothed could be together and bear children properly. But they had not. She had left Nazareth in haste to be with her cousin, Elisabeth, and on her return three months later, he knew. His Mary was with child!

In his shame that night, he had picked up a thick branch and smashed it against the bole of a tree, splintering it into a hundred fragments. Then he stood there, his face in his hands, shaking.

How lovely she had seemed, how fair, like a garden enclosed, with no spot on her. He had turned his drawn face upward, eyes pinched shut, beseeching the Lord for light.

And what did the law say? Why, put her away speedily! Disown her and make void the betrothal. Leave Mary to disgrace and grief. Sit in judgment on that new life and ordain condemnation. That was man's way out, the way of upright men, of earthlings built of dust and pride. And yet . . . "There is a way which seemeth right unto a man, but the end thereof are the ways of death. . . . Be not righteous overmuch . . . For love is strong . . . Pride goeth before destruction . . ."

No, he did not want to make her a public example. He was a just man. He was minded to put her away privately. Yet he did not. He could not.

Then, in a dream, out of the depths of his understanding, it came, sure wisdom, a message from the Lord:

"Joseph, thou son of David, fear not to take unto thee Mary thy wife: for that which is conceived in her is of the Holy Ghost. And she shall bring forth a son, and thou shalt call his name Jesus: for he shall save his people from their sins."

Distress there was, but it became a threshold of joy. With great gladness, he rose from his bed the next day, and took Mary as his wife, and her time drew nigh, and sweetness like a song was in his house.

When the emperor's decree went out for the census, he did not leave her alone, but took her with him, and the dust of the road, of the eighty-four miles, did not oppress them, and she sat the burro smiling at her Joseph.

After the child was born, they remained in Bethlehem, not returning to Nazareth. Joseph found work with his adze and his mallet, and a shelter for his family. He hewed wood from the acacia groves outside the town, and made benches and tables and plowshares.

The child grew healthy and strong, his eyes learning to pick out individual shapes and faces, to notice and distinguish, his lips forming those untrained smiles that spring from some original spark in human life. He quickened in mind and body, learning to guide his arms, to clasp with his fingers, experimenting with sound, babbling and cooing, saying his first near-words, pulling himself to his feet in his crib, loudly proclaiming his appetites and discomforts, sprouting his first teeth.

Joseph wrought at his bench beside the house, shaping his own boards from timber as carpenters had to do, smoothing with his adze and the chisel. He made carts and ox yokes, and stout, straight poles to pull the loads, and plows, cutting them to a V-point with an iron tip nailed to the edge. He toiled steadfastly, his great hands scarred from many cuts and bruises, his shoulders and arms hard from the axe, the bik-hammer and the knife, the sweat coursing down his cheeks into his gray beard. And on the Sabbath he worshiped and jounced Jesus on his knees.

Then the astonishing visitors arrived, the learned astrologers from afar. They had come by camel, across deserts and mountains, from Chaldea, Persia or farther in the Orient, from fifteen hundred miles or more, and their camels made growling sounds before the house, as the Magi tapped their necks, making them kneel, gradually drop to their bellies and pull their legs beneath them.

The scholars rejoiced at seeing the child and his mother, and knelt before him. Then from their camel baskets they brought gifts of gold and precious incense, frankincense and myrrh. Joseph had never seen the like of them.

But then, like a dark cloud, the shadow had moved across their little clay-brick house in Bethlehem, and now they trudged across a foreign land, many miles from home.

Each dawn, they went on, leg-sore and burned by the wind, halting at watering places, sleeping in the open amid the bedouins with their bright-colored tents and sleek, spirited horses. In alien towns, they replenished their foodstuffs. Along the roads were camels, laden with beams, and donkeys carrying skins of honey and bags of wheat, slaves bearing the palanquins of their masters, shepherds driving their flocks. Joseph and Mary kept going, wiping the dust from the face of the child they loved.

Well beyond the borders of Herod's kingdom, in the Sinai peninsula ruled by Egypt, or perhaps even deeper into the country, at last they halted, weary to the bone. With the gold of the Magi, they had ample money to obtain lodging at a caravansary. The flight was over.

There they remained awhile. They saw the alien sights, the rich Egyptians in their varicolored array of scarlet, yellow and green, with intricate patterns of leaves and animals, and their jangling beads and bracelets. Wheat fields covered the countryside, and brown-skinned fellahin worked antlike across them from dawn to dark. Some things were shocking to behold: the shrines to weird animallike gods, with images half-human and half-cat or goat or hippopotamus; the processions of chanting eunuch priests and corps of pagan temple prostitutes.

Time passed, and again Joseph pondered what to do in shepherding the life of the boy, who now toddled about well on his own feet. Again, as it had happened before, Joseph found his guidance in that house of dreams. A voice came:

"Arise, and take the young child and his mother, and go into the land of Israel: for they are dead which sought the young child's life." Herod the Great was no more.

So they departed. Out of Egypt they traveled back over the route they had come before. Out of Egypt, as told in the ancient prophecy, God had called his Son. They journeyed back toward the high country of Judea, of Bethlehem and Jerusalem.

But then they learned that Archelaus, a murderous son of Herod, now ruled there, and two thousand Jews had been crucified, three thousand slain in riots and thirty thousand sold into slavery. To safeguard his family, Joseph changed their course and destination. He led them westward toward the sea, and they traveled north along the coast, through Samaria, and returned to their old home in the fertile lowlands of Galilee. Back to Nazareth.

In the newly disjoined kingdom, another, milder son of Herod, called Herod Antipas, ruled in Galilee, and they were safe. There Joseph taught the boy gently and well the trade of his hands, and the words of the Scripture as commanded by the Lord:

". . . these words . . . thou shalt teach . . . diligently unto thy children, and shalt talk of them when thou sittest in thine house, and when thou walkest by the way, and when thou liest down, and when thou risest up."

There was abundant labor, for Herod Antipas was building a new capital at Sepphoris, just a short walk from Nazareth. So Joseph worked, with the saw and the bow and drill, with gnarled, veined hands, and he taught the boy well.

Oh, Joseph, of the great heart, wearing goodness and understanding. You are strong, Joseph, a man of toil, of gnarled hands and faith and wise judgment. For a short moment long ago, you hesitated before this child, but then, in fullest love, you battled for him mightily, and won.

You will endure, Joseph, for out of homeless nights and weary journeys and strength and sacrifice for a child, you built not beams and trestles, but life. Old carpenter,

JOSEPH

it is said you died in Jesus' early manhood, but the structure that you raised lives on beyond the best of wood. You
did not know at first, Joseph. But that boy was yours
because you wanted him, and is yours, even as he is all
mankind's who want him.

5

SALOME

*"And the child grew, and waxed strong in
spirit, filled with wisdom . . ."*

AS THEY APPROACHED the fork of the
road, Salome slyly nudged her burro ahead.
She didn't want Zebedee to see her doing it.
He always said a steady pace, not sprints
and starts, was the way to get anywhere. She partly lifted
herself on the riding pad, trying to see farther up the road.
Joy be! She could see them. At least a group was up there,
waiting in the shade of a big carob tree. It must be the
party from Nazareth. She believed she could recognize
her sister,* Mary, and there were several youngsters scam-
pering about. One of them must be Jesus.

Salome made clucking sounds in her throat and
reached back to slap her idling burro on the rump. He
sped ahead for a moment, then slowed down to his monot-
onous walk. Salome wriggled impatiently. She could go
faster than this on foot.

---

* In Biblical usage, *sister* or *brother* may connote *cousin* or other close
relationship. See *Author's Note.*

But she could see the people up there well now, and one of them . . . it must be, yes, it was Mary . . . walking out a little way toward her. Salome forgot herself and gouged the donkey in the ribs. He bolted ahead, and she clung to the strap, hearing Zebedee growl resignedly.

At the grassy roadside where Mary stood waiting, Salome jumped down and the two sisters rushed together, embracing. It had been many weeks since they had seen each other, and Salome was overjoyed. How wonderful Mary looked, and what pleasure they would have making this trip to Jerusalem together for the Passover, and how nicely the arrangements to meet here had worked out, and how were Jesus and Joseph? Oh, there they were over there. They certainly looked fine. The two sisters stood there holding each other's arms, smiling, Salome doing most of the talking.

She didn't notice that the rest of her group from Bethsaida and Capernaum had pulled up beside them, until she heard Zebedee's curt warning that they had better move along if they expected to reach Scythopolis by nightfall. But there were other kinspeople in the two parties, and it was some time before the greetings were over and Zebedee could prod them into resuming the journey.

They finally got lined out again, leaving the stragglers to catch up. Salome and her sister rode beside each other. Neither Mary's husband nor the boy, Jesus, had burros, so they walked. This always troubled Salome, since her own husband had a mount and owned burros to spare in their stable at home. Some of the other prosperous men also rode, as well as their wives. It was too bad for Joseph—he was getting rather old. Yet neither he nor the boy seemed to mind. They walked along in lightsome spirits, the boy pausing occasionally to examine a tortoise or explore a thicket, then running to overtake the group.

It was a festive company. Most of the burros were festooned with blue beads and red strips of wool dangling from their necks or halters. The riders sat sidewise. The women wore their best garments, tied about with colored girdles denoting their tribes, and flowing scarves over their heads. Zebedee's beard and hair, like some of the other wealthier men's, glistened with oil, even on the road. Their turbanlike sudaria fell back over their necks, and the robes of some of the men had wide, silken hems or fringes. Most of the youngsters skipped along in knee-length shirts.

Salome always looked forward to the two annual trips to Jerusalem—in the spring for the Passover and in the fall for the Feast of the Tabernacles or harvest. Scriptural law required the men to go, but Zebedee usually allowed her to go, too. It gave her a chance to be with Mary, besides being an adventuresome holiday. Members of the same clans from different towns customarily joined each other along the way, increasing the company as it moved toward the city.

Leaning toward her sister, Salome remarked how much Mary's son had grown, what a robustly alert youngster he seemed. Mary smiled, pleased, and inquired about Salome's sons. She had two, James and John, a little younger than Jesus, not yet old enough to begin their festival duties.

Jesus, at the age of twelve, had reached the *naar*

period of childhood—meaning the lad who shakes himself free. This was the next-to-last stage designated in Jewish childhood, each requiring its special understanding and tender care. Jesus had already passed the *yeled*, or new-born-babe period, and the *yoneq* suckling period before Salome ever had a chance to see him.

By the time Mary and Joseph had returned to Nazareth from Egypt, the boy must have been reaching the end of the *olel* phase, when he began to ask for solid food; or—she couldn't be sure—he might already have been a *gamul*, a weaned child more than two years old. Since then, she had been with him quite frequently and observed his growing up, through the *taph* stage, the child clinging to its mother; the *elem*, the child becoming firm; and now, the strapping *naar*.

Whenever Zebedee would permit it, Salome would take a servant or two and go for a visit with her sister in Nazareth. It not only enabled her to be with Mary for a time, but gave her some respite from Zebedee's fierce temper, much as she loved him, the volcano! (Her own boys seemed to have inherited some of that.) But she doubted if he even missed her on these family visits. He was always in such a commotion about his fishing fleet, his crews, his sales and shipments, buying new equipment, hiring cutters, expanding his wharves at Bethsaida and Capernaum, that he never would go with her. Besides, Zebedee would have been uncomfortable in Joseph and Mary's small, bare house in Nazareth, and he considered Joseph a mere laborer, a drudging artisan, not much of a success.

It was too bad Mary's husband hadn't been able to provide her with more possessions and standing. Salome valued these things greatly, and Zebedee had given them to her. She sometimes felt sorry that Mary had to do with scantier means. However, the family in Nazareth always seemed truly happy and buoyant. There were never any of the sharp outbursts of Salome's own big and bumptious household. Mary had to work harder, but she made no fuss about it. Without servants, she had to do her own grinding on the millstones, her own preserving and weaving.

Their house in Nazareth was a little one, built of limestone from the adjoining hills, with a beaten clay floor and niches in the walls for dishes and bedding. The roof consisted of pole rafters, covered with branches and brush, then topped with a thick, flat layer of clay. After every rainy spell, they had to go up on the roof and repack the loosened mud with a stone roller kept up there, and they had to tamp the sides.

Unlike arrangements in Salome's own home, where she and Zebedee had short-legged upholstered couches in their sleeping chamber, Joseph and Mary slept on mattresses of rushes on the floor, and the boy, too, after he left the crib. Overhead at night, Salome could hear the mice, scorpions and snakes rustling in the brush of the roof, and one morning a spider dangled down near her. She squealed, but the family just grinned at her. It wasn't unusual.

They took their meals sitting on sheepskin rugs on the floor. Joseph had built a low table, although most poorer families didn't have one. Most of their lamps were mere saucers of olive oil, with wicks drawn through floating corks. They ate from common dishes, using their fingers or dipping with a gourd from the bowls of onion and garlic soup, the wooden platters of fish, pickled or fried in little rolls of dough, the plates of lentils, radishes, olives, rice cakes and fruit. Most of the cooking was done outside over a grate. Sometimes they dined on bread dipped in spiced milk. They seldom had meat except on feast days, although now and then they managed it when Salome came, usually mutton or young kid.

Mary's boy was a tractable, well-behaved youngster, readily absorbing proper manners, learning it was not good to speak much while eating, that one should hold the cup a little in the hand before drinking, that it was rude to wipe the bottom of the plate.

But he also was a lion cub of energy and curiosity, romping through the groves of fig trees, pears and pomegranates, digging and building in the red dirt, staring open-mouthed at a crane or heron in flight, scrambling about to pick up olives while his mother shook them down from a tree with willow wands, racing ahead of her to fetch water from the spring beneath the hill. To this abundant well all the mothers of Nazareth came, carrying their water jars atop their heads.

Salome observed how sedulously Mary trained the boy, from the very beginning. Of course, all children were taught from the time of swaddling clothes to recognize God as their Father and Maker of the world. The commandments were engraved in their hearts. Mary, however, seemed especially attentive to her youngster, telling him the history of his tribe and clan, teaching him little prayers and the Psalms for the days of the week and festivals.

As a little *taph*, Jesus would watch Mary with interest as she went about her religious duties, lighting the Sabbath lamps, laying aside a portion of dough from the bread of the household, fixing the Mezuzah to the doorpost—the little folded parchment of verses bearing the name of the Most High. Everyone touched it on entering or leaving the house, then kissed his fingers. It was a symbol of divine guardianship over all Jewish homes. "The Lord shall preserve thy going out and thy coming in from this time forth, and even for evermore."

Salome loved the clean, bright atmosphere of Nazareth, perched high on the edge of a great valley. From the crest of the slope, you could see eastward to the Jordan and the mountains of Gilead beyond, and to the west, the blue of the Mediterranean in the distance. She and Mary, with little Jesus, would often walk up there and just stand, gazing. It was like looking at a whole world.

Salome's own town squatted down by the Galilee lake, six hundred feet below sea level, with its marshes, swamps, mosquitoes and fevers. And the houses there were of somber black lava rock. But Nazareth stood sixteen hundred feet above the sea; and its limestone houses, although tiny and plain, had a sunny, restful appearance there among the softly rounded hills.

Most of its people were poor. Joseph, as a laborer, earned only a drachma (twenty cents) or two a day. But he worked strenuously. The boy, as he grew older, would climb into the hills with him to cut trees, his muscles growing as hard as the wood they cut. They would come back, puffing and sweating, both they and the burro dragging great logs to be hewn into planks and posts and yokes and plows. Even when Joseph worked for hire on public buildings in nearby towns, he kept up his own trade in Nazareth.

The boy's regular schooling began when he was about five. Nazareth lacked the institutions of the greater cities, but it had its synagogue, where the youngsters would sit in a semicircle about the teacher, the chazan, who imparted to them the law "tempered by strictness with kindness." Up to the age of ten, the Scriptures constituted the only textbook, beginning with Leviticus, and then going on to other books of the law and prophets. They were stamped into the memory, woven into the conscience.

From about the age of ten to fifteen, the youngsters received instruction in the Mishnah, the oral traditions and interpretations of the law. Jesus was in this period now. Often, the older students gathered outdoors on a hillside or in a shaded clearing.

Watching Jesus grow up, Salome could foresee the changes in her own sons. As they would learn their father's fishing business, Jesus mastered the skills of a woodworker, getting so that he could judge the grain at a glance or a touch, his finger tips knowing instinctively the stress that could be applied to any point, learning to balance and shape for lasting strength. It was a trade of both hard manual labor and painstaking care, of weary backs, tired arms and smashed thumbs, of exactingly smoothed joints and mortises, of the rhythm of the shearing adze, of the fine eye of measuring line and rod, the stroke of saw and bik-hammer, the bite of wedge, the hot, whirring grind of bow and drill.

But Jesus, like the other youngsters, had time for frolic, to chase through the vineyards and fields, to fish in the lake an hour's walk away, to learn to hurl from a sling with accuracy. At harvest times, the town's children made a game of tramping barefoot on the grapes in the wine press, shrilling in their soggy dance. They did the same on the cut wheat to thresh it on a public floor or rooftop.

Since no main routes ran through Nazareth, it was the rare occasion when traveling merchants came there, peddling such luxuries as Phoenician purple or ginger from India. Then all the town would turn out. Afterward it would return to its simple ways, its dirt streets trodden only by its rural inhabitants, an occasional flock of sheep moving to a new pasture, or an oxcart loaded with melons.

It thus was doubly exciting for Joseph and Mary to make the trip to Jerusalem, and for the boy, too.

Salome could read the excitement on their faces during the journey, and as they entered the great city, she watched them, slyly amused. Joseph and Mary held each other's hand tightly, as if for reassurance, and their heads whipped rapidly about at the sights and sounds, their expressions flickering alternately with uncertain smiles and astonishment.

The boy, Jesus, was wordless. He seemed to be taking it all in with calm thoughtfulness. Questioning lines formed on his smooth, bronzed forehead as he gazed about at the babbling, banging, assorted traffic, the gaudily arrayed rich, the groveling poor, the children with bloated bellies and stringy limbs, the mothers with clipped heads trying to sell their hair to buy bread, the bland-faced priests in glittering regalia, the soldiers, the pipers to snakes, the street dancers, the pious Pharisees praying aloud on street corners, the worn-out workers with dogs licking their sores, the near-naked slaves with tags of ownership chained about their necks.

Salome became absorbed in watching the boy's reactions. He acted neither pleased nor distraught, neither awed nor bored, only puzzled, a little confused. Salome thought of her own sons, and imagined they would be jumping up and down, either scared, angry or gleeful. But Jesus was only quietly observant, as if studying some new, peculiar object he had never seen before.

Zebedee and Salome took a room at a hostelry during the week, and Joseph and Mary pitched their tent with thousands of other pilgrims outside the city walls. However, they took their Passover supper together, and Salome and Mary arranged for the two families to meet on various occasions at the Temple during the festival. At its close, their large band reassembled and started back to Galilee.

They had gone a full day's journey when Mary became worried about Jesus. Presumably he was back with the other youngsters, who often trailed along in a group. But Mary insisted on looking, and Salome went with her. Jesus wasn't among them. Mary became alarmed. She told Joseph, and they both ranged back and forth along the line of travelers, calling Jesus' name. He couldn't be found.

Finally the whole party halted, and a thorough search was made. Other youngsters were questioned. None had seen Jesus all day. The other mothers began moaning sympathetically, *haval, haval*, woe, woe! Mary's chin quivered, and she began crying softly. Joseph took her firmly by the shoulders. They would find the boy, he said. Do not fear. They must return to the city.

Salome wanted to accompany them, but Zebedee quickly refused. Reluctantly she watched Mary and Joseph start back alone, while the rest of the party continued on northward. Zebedee remarked that these latter-day descendants of David didn't seem very efficient with their own affairs. Salome, sulking, made no reply.

It was later that she learned what had happened. Mary and Joseph began their hunt in the most likely place, the camp outside the city, threading through its improvised shops, tents, and garbage heaps and its moil of people. Wherever children played, they paused, noting each figure. They went into the city, tramping up one street and down another, back and forth, asking questions, their hearts sinking at the brusque rejoinders, pushing through the crowded markets and into the back streets and twisting lanes of the lower city, glancing into shops, inquiring of watchmen and gatekeepers.

For three days they searched, scarcely stopping to eat or sleep, a million dire possibilities crossing their minds. They wandered through the tunnels below the Temple and climbed into its rectilinear maze of courts, moving in and out among the crowds, their eyes glazed from look-ing. Finally, they stood on one of the outer Temple porches, weak, despairing, strained to the breaking point.

Just down the columned porch, a group of learned doctors, great scholars of theology and law, were deeply engrossed in conversation. Mary and Joseph stared at them leadenly. Then a sound caught their ears. Their heads jerked up. It was a boy's voice, serious and inquiring. Jesus! With one accord, they rushed across the floor and then they saw him there in the center of the bearded sages. One of them turned, shushing Mary and Joseph. For just a moment, Mary leaned on Joseph's shoulder, flooded with unutterable relief. Blessed God be praised! There was her son, well and hearty as could be, his face upturned, frown-ing slightly, listening and asking questions of the famous rabbis, astonishing them with his comprehension and per-ceptive comments.

But he had no right to cause his parents such anxiety. Mary pushed through the group and confronted him sternly. "Son, why hast thou thus dealt with us? behold, thy father and I have sought thee sorrowing."

He looked up at her with innocent appeal. "How is it that ye sought me? wist ye not that I must be about my Father's business?"

Mary pursed her lips, unmoved by his excuse. She took his hand, and she and Joseph led him away. Neither of them saw any basis for his explanation. They took him home to Nazareth, and life returned to its normal, quiet pace, the boy as obedient as ever. The incident had not lessened his filial dutifulness or response to discipline.

Salome heard all about it on her next visit, and she began to notice that the boy, although as full of vim and bursting enthusiasms as any other youngster, became increasingly meditative as he grew older. Despite his hardy physique and manly labors now, he had a sensitive nature, quick to react and sympathize.

He was a *naar* no longer, but a *bachur*, a ripened one, and then a man, increased in wisdom and stature.

In his leisure time, he would stroll into the hills and join the shepherds with their flocks, or stop to talk with the farmers, sometimes hanging a bag on his shoulder to help them sow, or borrowing a flint-edged sickle to help them cut their wheat or barley. In Nazareth, children would bring their toys for his nimble fingers to repair.

Although the sages enjoined every Jewish young man to take a wife by the age of eighteen, Jesus showed no inclination to do so, but his kindly interest in women, young and old, attracted them to him. He became acquainted with landlords and servants, the respected and the shunned. In nearby Sepphoris, which Herod Antipas had turned into a cosmopolitan center of Greek culture—the "ornament of all Galilee"—Jesus met stewards and noblemen, Gentiles, artists, the rich and oppressed.

But mostly he spent his time in the tender hills around Nazareth, studying, responding to the good air and the earth and simple joys, watching a marten scamper through the cedars, or spying a deer or ibex on the skyline. He would sit for hours, admiring a swath of yellow marguerites or blooming laurel or lilies of the valley. Sometimes he would disappear into the hills for several days at a time.

Salome always had been touched by the winsome Jesus; and when his ministry began, drawing her own sons into its orbit, she was among the first to sense his transcendent greatness. Like most others, she did not understand it clearly, and in her bubbling animation and regard for social status, she once asked Jesus to be sure and give her sons high rank in his royal court. Yet the fact that Jesus ascended no golden stairs and put on no kingly coronet did not stop Salome from serving him, following him all the way. Instead of the heights, he assailed the depths. And among the few who stayed with him to the end was Salome. Oh, yes, she had her womanly interest in fine things and elevated position, but it did not keep her from loving him, and believing, even later in his awful straits— no more than it had ever stemmed her abounding affection for those poor relations of hers in Nazareth.

6

JOHN THE BAPTIST

". . . the kingdom of heaven is at hand."

OUT OF THE DESERT he came. Out of the brooding rocks and sand, out of the flaming sun, John the Baptist came striding, his eyes on fire and his shaggy mane a banner in the wind.

"Prepare ye the way of the Lord . . ."

Down from the hills he came. Down from the crags and dunes and burning wastelands. Down from the region of the serpent and the thorn, he came, raising his arms like spiny branches to the sky.

"Make straight the way of the Lord!"

From the wilderness west of the Dead Sea, the prophet came down to the Jordan's banks, wrapped in a camel's pelt tied with leather thongs, bearing the secrets of long silence and the stars. "There cometh one mightier than I after me," he proclaimed, "the latchet of whose shoes I am not worthy to stoop down and unloose. I indeed have baptized you with water: but he shall baptize you with the Holy Ghost."

John had no inkling who the mighty one would be, as he trumpeted his tidings there on the green banks of the Jordan, rallying the startled populace. But the conviction seethed within him, and he knew the moment of the Lord would shortly come. While he waited, he lashed out at the cruelties, the greed, the sham and vainglories that despoiled the earth.

"Repent ye!" he cried.

Some heard. Some closed their ears in scorn. They came from far and near, the curious, the hostile and the hopeful, the tax-gouging publicans, the farmers from the wayside, the Roman soldiers in their bell-shaped weather coats of leather, the finicky Pharisees, the ragged families from their caves, the spies of the powerful Sadducees, the skeptics, the wayward Herodian youths with their Greek manners and broad-brimmed hats.

"O generation of vipers," John blazed at them, stabbing a finger toward the nether world, "who hath warned you to flee from the wrath to come?"

With passion and with lancing words, with no awe for rank or station, he roared against the proud, the cheats, the selfish rich, the doers of violence, the wickedness of kings. And all the while, his sun-seasoned, squinting eyes searched the horizon and scanned their faces, convinced that soon the staff of God would rise among them.

John the Baptist was a battler with a flaming vision. For years, he had stayed in the barren uplands, listening to the cadences of eternity, watching the wind trace its mysterious symmetries in the sand, seeing the sunsets turn to blood and fire, hearing the lonely nights make conversation. He had been born some thirty years before to dignified, respected parents, the priest, Zacharias, and his wife, Elisabeth, in their advanced age, and he never forgot the stirring prediction of his father. Each time the words came to him they were like metal and stone striking new fire: "And thou, child, shalt be called the prophet of the Highest: for thou shalt go before the face of the Lord to prepare his ways; to give knowledge of salvation unto his people by the remission of their sins . . ."

In his youth, the keen-eyed, virtuous John smoldered at the injustices, the wanton vogues and the violence that swirled around him. The world's heathenism, devoid of any compassion, crept into the little island of Judaism, spreading brutality, license and exploitation. Polygamy abounded. Men divorced their wives at will. Young men, imitating the pagans of Greece and Rome, shaved their faces, and young girls scented their hair with marjoram and stained their lips with alkanet root. In the arena at Jerusalem animals screamed in massive slaughter to entertain the multitude.

Victims of war or debt, thousands toiled in slavery, in the ditches and households—about three slaves to every citizen. Their offspring were discarded to die. Many were herded in chains into the copper mines to hack and haul until blinded by the metallic dust, then to be cast aside like slag. The breadless poor huddled in their caves, selling their young into harlotry or bondage. The sick and the beggars, their tatters revealing sores on their flesh, lay like rubble in the alleys and beside the Temple porches. Kings and priests exacted their heavy tribute: a third of a farmer's grain, crown taxes, Temple taxes, stores and cattle seized for war, levies for first fruits, gratitude and guilt, tithes and second tithes and sacrifices. The rich grew richer with their rubies, pearls, emeralds and golden goblets, and the poor more destitute.

Amidst the clangorous forces and collapsing ideals, Judaism, the olden beacon of the one God, split into contending factions. The studious Pharisees with their precise piety elaborated law until it became a hollow shell, naming thirty-nine deeds as Sabbath work, declaring a man must carry no burden on that day heavier than a fig. The Sadducees, those wealthy tools of Rome who ruled the priesthood, turned the Temple into a place of commerce. They used the lash to impose their will. Fierce Zealots carried daggers and swore death to all disloyal Jews.

Against it all John had rebelled. As a young man, he had quit his priestly home, his doting parents, and gone into the wilderness. He had vanished into an arid, solitary landscape of mountains and sand, and there for perhaps ten years he remained, living on locusts and wild honey.

Many Jews, in dismay at the perversities and grinding oppression, had fled like him into isolation—the Covenanters of Damascus to northern Israel, the Therapeutae Covenanters to their abodes in Egypt, the Essenes or "bathers" to their caves beside the Dead Sea, where about four thousand of them studied their scrolls of Scripture, adhering to strict manuals of discipline, spending their days in meditation, looking toward the coming of a wondrous "Teacher of Righteousness."

To this same realm of solitude went John the Baptist. But his was an individual mission, a special destiny. It entwined him and governed him as he sat musing on a rocky knoll, or wandered the wind-swept plateaus, or knelt praying beside a scraggly juniper.

There, through the years of inner scruntiny, of purifying his judgements and sharpening his senses, he had waited for the time when he would be called forth. There in that place of sun and sand, of singing silences, with the stars caressing the very hills at night, he had held his long consultation with the infinite. And when, at last, the voice of the spirit rang in him like a command, he marched down from his fastnesses, a thunderhead out of the west, a blazing harbinger of a new kingdom.

A hard, dark figure of skin and bones, this coarsely garbed desert prophet shook the region roundabout like an avalanche. From Galilee to the north, and Judea and Jerusalem to the south, and from Peraea they came, drawn by his swift, straight words, his fearless rebukes of the mighty, his attacks on the swindlers, his demands for decency and dignity and generosity toward men.

And all the while, with certainty pulsing in his blood, he kept telling them that God soon would send his emissary, who would be like a thresher on a wheat floor fanning out the chaff from the grain. ". . . he will burn up the chaff with unquenchable fire. . . . Bring forth therefore fruits meet for repentance . . ." he cried.

John yearned and waited and wondered, his piercing

eyes probing the distant mountains. How? When? Who? Many came to him, confessing, and were baptized in the river. Others questioned him, and he flung back his answers, trim as spears.

"What shall we do then?" they asked.

"He that hath two coats, let him impart to him that hath none," the Baptist declared.

The publican toll collectors asked, "What shall we do?"

"Exact no more than that which is appointed you."

The Roman soldiers asked, "And what shall we do?"

"Do violence to no man, neither accuse any falsely; and be content with your wages."

The hard-swinging Baptist, in a thrust that later would cost him dearly, denounced Galilee's King Herod Antipas for expelling his first wife and taking in her place Herodias, his niece as well as wife of his half-brother Philip, who ruled a northern tetrarchy. Railing at this incestuous, adulterous marriage, he declared that if he were face to face with the immoral monarch he would give him this blunt message: "It is not lawful for thee to have thy brother's wife."

There was a stir in the crowd, and a knot of men in courtly dress broke away and started off in the direction of the capital of Galilee at Tiberias. This bothered John not at all. He was a man purged by his long solitude of the pressures, timidities and subservience that controlled the world, and he wore the breastplate of invincible purpose, sure that he would not be swerved from its fulfillment.

Not long afterward as he preached on the river bank,

his eyes fell on one face and lingered there. He recognized the man from the years of his youth. It was Jesus, the son of his mother's cousin, Mary of Nazareth. An odd sensation came over John, and his words, for once, faltered. Needles of light danced in the air, and he could not be sure they were from the sun or in his mind. He was disconcerted, excited, puzzled.

He remembered Jesus as keenly intelligent, with an unerring sense of justice and a candor that enabled him to shear away the husk of a question and get quickly at its kernel. With all that, he was gentle, a friend to all, modest, gracious. John, of a more withdrawn disposition, had wished at times he could emulate his cousin, even though Jesus was younger by six months.

As the prophet continued now with his discourse, a bit disconnectedly, an obscure, prickling demand formed in him. It made him ill at ease. He licked his cracked lips and tried to regain the vigor of his normal speech. But his thoughts clouded, and his gaze kept returning to Jesus, who stood there relaxed, his head cocked a little to one side, listening benignly to whatever John would say. The Baptist could not understand what moved him so acutely, with such insistence. He had never been affected in this way before, never been stumbling in his delivery. Even though his youthful admiration for Jesus might have amounted almost to envy, he had always sincerely loved him, and his presence should not so distract him. The impulses he felt now included love, but something else besides.

John ran a bony hand through his hair, took a deep

breath and tried to concentrate on his subject. But the feeling of inadequacy kept sweeping in on him. It was as if something were needed of him that he had not given; something required that he had not provided; something to do that he had not done. And his attention kept swinging back to Jesus.

He and Jesus differed greatly in temperament. John was the rigid purist, never touching strong drink, unable to stand the presence of evil, inflexible in its condemnation. Jesus on the other hand was innately sociable, mixing with all sorts of people, good and bad, using kindly interest as his instrument instead of scathing diatribe. John, the ascetic, abhorred the sight of sin, and withdrew from it. Jesus went to meet it.

The unfamiliar reactions in John continued now even as, somewhat haltingly, he continued to speak. He folded his hands at his chest, praying inwardly. The divine guidance which he had found in the wilderness and to which he attuned his being seemed to be bidding him to act, to make manifest. He had an urge to exclaim, There he stands among you! He wanted to point to Jesus and extol him. But it seemed incredible. Had he, John, been chosen by God to prepare the way for one he had known since childhood? Had it taken him this long odyssey of the spirit to recognize what had been so near? Was this the end of his vigil?

When he had concluded his sermon, some of the hearers approached to offer repentance and be baptized. Among them was Jesus. John, blinking his eyes, demurred at the prospect. He blurted, "I have need to be baptized of thee, and comest thou to me?"

Clasping John by the shoulders fondly, Jesus looked into the craggy, dark face. "Suffer it to be so now," he urged quietly, "for thus it becometh us to fulfil all righteousness."

John led Jesus down into the sluggish waters of the Jordan, a sense of awareness and discovery surging through him. Not a ripple stirred on the quiet current. But as John baptized him, a whirring as from many wings filled his ears, like a wind in forest foliage, like a rushing across the breast of the water. Then in the still sunlight a white dove circled serenely down and perched on Jesus' shoulder. "This is my beloved Son, in whom I am well pleased." John heard it, his heart racing, the voice seeming to glide down from the heavens as peacefully and affectionately as the dove.

John scrambled up out of the river, his hairy coat dripping, his words crackling with their old passion, only now instinct with triumph. "This is he of whom I said," he shouted, extending his arm toward Jesus, "After me cometh a man which is preferred before me: for he was before me. And I knew him not . . ."

Jesus came up out of the water and stood there a moment, his lips compressed, his brow furrowed in thought, as if some new, heavy burden had come upon him, hardly noticing John or the people, but the Baptist talked on, his voice ecstatic. "Behold the Lamb of God, which taketh away the sin of the world," he cried. "And I knew him not: but he that sent me to baptize with water, the same said unto me, Upon whom thou shalt see the Spirit descending, and remaining on him, the same is he which baptizeth with the Holy Ghost. And I saw, and bare record that this is the Son of God."

Jesus walked slowly away, following a path that rose up from the riverbank. They could see him silhouetted briefly against the sky and then the figure dwindled and disappeared.

The Baptist stood there for a long time, silently. He had finished his work. He had served his lifelong purpose. He had heralded the coming of the Lord.

In the ensuing days, he continued to preach and baptize, but his ardor and the crowds shrank. He spoke mostly of Jesus. ". . . the law was given by Moses, but grace and truth came by Jesus Christ. No man hath seen God at any time; the only begotten Son, which is in the bosom of the Father, he hath declared him."

Agents of the Sadducees, alarmed at the reports emanating from the outlands, came from Jerusalem to challenge John, to demand who he claimed to be, Elijah or, if not, who? "I am not," John snapped. "I am not the Christ. . . . I am the voice of one crying in the wilderness . . . but there standeth one among you, whom ye know not . . ."

Weeks later, when Jesus himself began to preach, John realized even more that his own duty was done. His disciples even complained about Jesus. "Rabbi," they said, ". . . all men come to him."

The Baptist, sorry to see them disappointed, sought to explain to them how Jesus was not a rival, but the prime mover. ". . . the friend of the bridegroom . . . re-joiceth greatly because of the bridegroom's voice: this my joy therefore is fulfilled. He must increase, but I must decrease."

It could not be otherwise, should not be otherwise, he said. His own star was setting. "He that cometh from above is above all: he that is of the earth . . . speaketh of the earth . . . he whom God hath sent speaketh the words of God . . . The Father loveth the Son, and hath given all things into his hand."

There was a touching sadness as the Baptist faded into the background. Not long after he had accomplished his goal, men of Herod Antipas seized him and hauled him away to Machaerus Fortress as an insurrectionist. In prison, cut off from the wide-open sky and earth where he had found his strength, worries assailed him, and he sent a message to Jesus, asking, "Art thou he that should come? Or look we for another?"

Jesus sent back word reassuring him, describing his work and ending with a gentle appeal: ". . . blessed is he, whosoever shall not be offended in me."

A little later, at the instigation of Herodias, whose marriage the Baptist had dared criticize, he was decap-itated, and his head brought to the palace to placate her and the king's dancing daughter. John's disciples came to the fortress prison to claim his body.

"Among those that are born of women," Jesus said, "there is not a greater prophet than John the Baptist . . ."

The angry, rugged Baptist left his mark on many,

for twenty years later followers spoke of him in far-off Ephesus. He had prepared the way, set the foundations. The voice in the wilderness, a lonely cry on the border of a raucous, reeling world, had lit the lamp of his Lord, and the light would one day illuminate the earth.

7

JOSES

*"And he came to Nazareth, where he had
been brought up . . ."*

WE HAD NOT SEEN HIM for forty
days. It worried us. Despite his re-
sourcefulness and dependability, we
could not help being concerned about
where he might be or how he fared. He had walked off
alone into the uninhabited, sun-seared wilderness, and there
had since been no word from him or about him, from anywhere. Yet we forebore from going to search for him.
Not because of any laxness, but because of him. Jesus had
a purposefulness about him that turned aside interference.
He would not be deterred.

He had always been one of us, but he was different.
He had a way of his own. He always had treated me
supremely, and I could not have asked for a better, more
loyal companion to grow up with, but sometimes I couldn't
quite make him out.

I was a younger member of the family, and I naturally admired him and looked up to him. But in spite of this deep attachment, I knew he also encompassed a zone I had never wholly grasped.

In our youth, I seldom realized the significance of the signs at his birth. I had heard other members of the line of David here in Nazareth allude to it privately, but to me, Jesus had always been just a good standby, an indulgent, older partner, a brotherly guide. As we advanced in adulthood, however, it seemed that the distance between us widened. The close ties slid away. Not that he was less devoted to the family or solicitous of our welfare, but that he also looked beyond us, with equal concern, to a broader circle.

I often felt at a loss to understand him, and I know others did, too. Here in this little town, with many of us proud of our Davidic ancestry, Jesus had always been well regarded, an affable and obliging young man, an excellent joiner of wood. But his remarks often took us aback. He had a penchant for cutting into old preconceptions and conventions which none of us had ever thought of questioning. And he always struck joltingly to the heart of the matter. This undoubtedly had nettled some of the town's older counselors. And truthfully, I was a bit befogged by it all. Ever since he was a boy of twelve, however, he had liked to engage the wise elders in discussion, and we had come to accept this as one of his exceptional traits.

My own interests had remained wholly ordinary—working, marrying, rearing a family. I favored our village, one of the few in the region with clear, pure water without the brackishness of the wells in surrounding towns, and I had no desire to seek adventure elsewhere.

Jesus, on the other hand, with his far-ranging absorption in the whole of life, and his peculiar sense of responsibility to it, gave no indication of settling down. In fact, as he neared the age of thirty, he seemed to become increasingly preoccupied and irregular. He often went apart to himself for long periods of prayer and study. He seemed intent on some inner working of conscience as if he confronted some important crossroads. He would sit rapt in meditation.

Then he had gone and been baptized by the hermit prophet, John the Baptist, who had been attracting many to his ministry by the Jordan. Immediately afterward, Jesus had disappeared into the wilderness, taking no food, no tent, nothing. As the time passed, our disquietude had increased. We knew that leopards, hyenas, wolves and other beasts prowled the hot sands and mountains into which he had gone, that the region offered no shelter to man.

But God must have sustained him. For finally, at the end of the forty days, he came back.

He was a changed person, sun-blackened, his bones showing through the tight, dry skin, his jaws shrunken, and strands of gray in his sand-matted hair and beard. Yet his eyes shone with tranquil strength. Whatever the tests or self-searching to which he had subjected himself there in the lone, cruel wastes, he had won. We could tell that in his eyes and in his glad voice. But he obviously had been without nourishment throughout the time, and he ate heartily. We were all greatly relieved.

Almost at once he went forth and began preaching in the neighboring towns of Galilee, with surprisingly stirring effect. Many acclaimed him and flocked to him. His fame ran through all the province.

Then, his physical condition much restored, he returned to Nazareth. We felt both pride and sensitivity about him. We knew that many in the village, having known him as a barefooted youngster and later as maker of their yokes and plows, doubted he could have any special endowment as a teacher. Some made jests about it. Some spoke jealously of him, saying he deceived strangers elsewhere. "Whence hath this man this wisdom, and these mighty works?" they said. ". . . is not his mother called Mary? and his brethren, James, and Joses, and Simon, and Judas? And his sisters, are they not all with us? Whence then hath this man all these things?" I overheard many such muffled remarks, and neighbors spoke such questions to me directly. I could not answer. I'm sure Jesus also sensed that they were offended by him.

But because of his successes in other towns, he was invited to read in the synagogue on the coming Sabbath. I was nervous as the time approached, and so were others in the family. Only Jesus seemed relaxed, happy at being home as in the former days.

Came the Sabbath, and we gathered in the little stone synagogue facing the Temple in Jerusalem. The women stood on one side, the men on the other. Jesus took the chair beside the reading desk at the front. Behind him on the platform, facing the congregation, sat the elders of the synagogue. All joined in reciting the great Shema, "Hear, O Israel . . ."

I must confess that I did not follow the prayers as reverently as one should that morning. I could detect the strain and cynicism in the room. The elders looked especially dour and watchful.

Jesus stood up behind the desk and laid out the scroll. He took his time in finding the place, his hands steady. No trace of the tension showed in his sun-browned face. The congregation became so hushed I could hear myself breathing. Jesus' gaze came up for a moment, falling serenely on the people. Then he began to read, first in Hebrew, then in the provincial Aramaic. I recognized the Scripture at once as from Isaiah 61. He read in clear, even tones:

"The Spirit of the Lord is upon me, because he hath anointed me to preach the gospel to the poor; he hath sent me to heal the brokenhearted, to preach deliverance to the captives, and recovering of sight to the blind, to set at liberty them that are bruised, to preach the acceptable year of the Lord."

He slowly rolled up the scroll, handed it to an attendant and sat down as customary to give his exposition of the passage. Every eye in the synagogue fastened on him. It seemed that, for the moment, the world had paused, its attention fixed on the traveling carpenter's son, come home proclaimed as rabbi.

Jesus let the suspense concentrate until it seemed about to burst. Then, his gentle gaze resting on the faces before him, his own countenance grave but firm, his voice exceedingly quiet but carrying to every corner of the room, he said:

"This day is this scripture fulfilled in your ears."

Nine words. And he stopped. His startling pronouncement, given first at home. There was a sound of sucked-in breaths, a wave of murmurs and exclamations. "Is not this Joseph's son?" a man burst out. How could he claim to be God's anointed? The shocking words left them reeling in mind. I had feared something like this and sat rigidly, wondering what to do, when Jesus' voice rose again. Oddly, they quieted.

"Ye will surely say unto me this proverb, 'Physician, heal thyself . . .'" He paused, sadly but unrelenting. "Verily I say unto you, No prophet is accepted in his own country. . . . A prophet is not without honour, but in his own country, and among his own kin, and in his own house."

I could feel their shock congealing now, their smoldering suspicions turning into open hostility. But he went on, adding coals to the flame, recalling how the prophet Elisha of old, at a time when his own people turned deaf ears to God's words, wrought his blessings elsewhere, even beyond Judaism, beyond people who counted themselves chosen, for others who were eager to hear and accept.

No one could have stopped what happened then. It was like a commotion of animals. The elders, the congregation, the men and women, jumped to their feet and surged about him, seizing him and thrusting him out of the synagogue. They shoved him along the street toward the outer edge of the city. I flailed about me, trying to stop them, crying out to them to stop, to consider, but my cries were lost in the wrathful shouting.

Then I saw where they were going—to the high bluff to hurl him to death. I grabbed first one and then another, begging them to help, but they cast me aside, and my pleas were useless in their frenzy. I fought my way through them and then was hauled backward again, but I caught a glimpse of Jesus' face, and he walked along unresisting, sorrowing but unangered. Then I could see him no more.

Some of them had laid hold on me, restraining me, and the herd moved on. They became quieter, more deadly quiet, as they neared the precipice, and I struggled in vain. Then they stopped, hesitating, and I saw him again, standing there facing them, his back to the great drop, his eyes burning into them, almost daring them. A majesty was upon him. The men suddenly had become speechless, motionless. There was a prolonged, stark moment, and then they seemed to shrink as if exposed to their own bestiality. He moved toward them, and they fell back, leaving a wide path. He passed through them. As he reached the place where I stood, he started to pause, then he smiled at me, a nostalgic, hurt smile, and went on, leaving Nazareth behind.

It had been a terrifying experience for Mary and indeed for all of us. And it left us even more deeply anxious about him, lest some worse assault befall him in another place.

Among some of the people of Nazareth the talk spread that he was beside himself, that he had gone mad.

Thereby they sought to vindicate their own delirious action and allay their consciences. So now they came to us in sympathy, saying these things, and offering to go and help fetch him.

This, too, dismayed our hearts. We knew of the crowds of people gone to hear him throughout Galilee, and from the Diaspora across the Jordan, and from Judea to the south and Jerusalem, and we also heard of the severe resentment of religious officials. We feared for him.

We longed to see him, and so we determined to go to talk with him. Perhaps he should be warned of the disapproval of many rabbis and synagogue rulers. Some friends went with us and his mother, who prayed daily for his peace and safety. We found him preaching to a huge gathering in the synagogue of Capernaum by the lake. People packed the building, and others crowded the entrance and street outside. We pressed in as closely as possible. Someone recognized us, and the whispered word traveled to the front of the synagogue, and a man informed him, "Behold, thy mother and thy brethren stand without, desiring to speak with thee."

Jesus looked back toward us, his eyes caressing us with that old, melting affection we knew so well, but then I could see that other responsibility working in him, that fixed, overriding dutifulness that transcended family and home and all things, that took him determinedly beyond us to a larger sphere, and he said: "Who is my mother? and who are my brethren?" He stretched out his arms to the many, unknown people from everywhere, and said to them, "Behold my mother and my brethren! For whosoever shall do the will of my Father which is in heaven, the same is my brother, and sister, and mother."

Then, truly, I knew how far he had moved beyond our own snug, enclosed little comradeship. His arms seemed to embrace far more than me and his own blood. He belonged not just to us, or to Nazareth, but to some indefinable, numberless family.

After that, his influence grew still more, and he won many thousands of believers in the towns of the province, from the lake to the Mediterranean coast, and he even preached in the heathen ports of Phoenicia to the north and in pagan country to the east, and his name became renowned in the region. He did amazing works of healing of the sick and despairing, and I began to take great pride in his successes, speaking of it to others. Although Jewish officials, especially the priesthood in Jerusalem, were highly incensed, he now had a strong following, and I thought he should go there for the coming Festival of the Tabernacles and make a great demonstration, establishing himself in the heart of Judaism, as he had done in Galilee. With some of our other brethren, I went to see him to urge this opportune course.

"Depart hence," I said, "and go into Judaea, that thy disciples also may see the works that thou doest. For there is no man that doeth any thing in secret, and he himself seeketh to be known openly. If thou do these things, shew thyself to the world." We brethren did not then believe in him as the Messiah, but did know he performed impressive works.

"My time is not yet come," he said, and put a hand

on my shoulder, "but your time is always ready. The world cannot hate you; but me it hateth, because I testify of it, that the works thereof are evil." He paused, and again I had that sensation that I no longer really knew him, that he had left me sometime back in our youth. He added, "Go ye up unto this feast: I go not up yet . . . for my time is not yet full come."

So we went. And it was later that we learned he had followed secretly, and of the indignities visited on him there, the threats of stoning, the attempts to intimidate him. We did not know then that the worst was still to come. And it was only after it came that we finally, belatedly, came to know him, to know the brother who had held my hand while I learned to walk, to know the meaning of those muted family secrets of years ago in Bethlehem, to know the Savior who "came unto his own, and his own received him not. But as many as received him, to them gave he power to become the sons of God, even to them that believe on his name. . . ."

Joses and the other brethren of Jesus later became leaders themselves in the faith which they were so long in recognizing, even though, or perhaps because, it nestled in their own backyard.

8

NATHANAEL

"And seeing the multitudes,
he went up into a mountain . . ."

THE DUST from many feet swirled about their heads as they trudged across the dry flat toward the base of the mountain. Nathanael coughed and wiped at his brow with a thin, moist hand. To him, much of all this lacked propriety.

From behind and on either side came the shuffling noise of the throng, the cries of children, the rustle of coarse garments, the mixed mumble of a barefoot multitude. Somewhere far to the rear rose the labored chant of a Psalm, "In thee, O Lord, do I put my trust . . ."

Nathanael's eyes watered, blinking at the grime; and the dust rose ahead like a red fog. Nothing seemed proper. Standards seemed out of order and gone askew. The whole affair had seemed illogical even at the start. And now, the decorous habits of his lifetime lay in disarray. Nathanael stumbled on a slab of earth, caught himself, and tramped on.

In the past several months, it seemed he had recast the very mold of his judgments. To think that he, Nathanael, righteous, discriminating, with cultured tastes, would dip from the same bowl with known sinners, touch the unclean, sleep in hovels without even a rug, pray over the pockmarked sick! Nathanael shook his head dazedly.

Some singular, puzzling influence kept him in this undertaking, and he knew from whence it sprang. He glanced at Jesus, striding along slightly in front of him. An uncommon man! Mild, yet dominant, compelling. Nathanael's throat filled. He loved this new Master. But Jesus had such irregular ways!

Time after time, Nathanael, and the others, too, had taken some action to maintain convention, to prevent annoyances for Jesus, or guard him from the rabble, only to have him choose the opposite course. But it all could have been expected. A twinge went through Nathanael. After all, Jesus came from that backward hamlet, Nazareth.

"Can there any good thing come out of Nazareth?" That, he recalled, had been his first, contemptuous reaction when his friend, Philip, first told him about Jesus. Nathanael, the young, polished scholar, discreet in his associates, scrupulous in manners, lived then in a fine orchard-ringed house at Cana, just three and a half miles northeast of Nazareth. And he had looked with disdainful condescension on that rustic village, with its rutted streets and unwhitened houses, as well as on its peasant inhabitants.

Yet here he was, a member of the little band of twelve, swept along before a motley horde of commonfolk, the rootless, poor *am-haaretz*, with their wind-burned, drawn faces, their bony limbs and rough, rope-girdled mantles. And Nathanael, despite his meticulous nature, could not shake off the spell of Jesus, the new, insistent leaven working in his mind. . . .

". . . many that are first shall be last; and the last shall be first. . . . for I was an hungred, and ye gave me meat . . . I was a stranger, and ye took me in: naked, and ye clothed me . . . in prison, and ye came unto me. . . ." All around, the low, massed clomp of naked feet hemmed in Nathanael like a wall. ". . . Inasmuch as ye have done it unto one of the least of these my brethren, ye have done it unto me."

The crowd streamed on across the flat swamp bed, crusted and bare in the dry season, and started up the shoulder of the mountain. A broiling sun beat down from a bleached sky, but as they climbed to higher ground, it offered a flutter of breeze, touching cool on Nathanael's perspiring skin. He brushed fastidiously at his short beard to free it of the dust.

Surely, some bounds must be set in dealing with these derelict creatures. Yet, each time, Jesus gave them attention. Nathanael sighed. When they had tried to get some rest by withdrawing to the Mediterranean ports of Tyre and Sidon, it had been the same. Most unseemly. Nathanael's exasperation surged anew.

There, in that dissolute region of Greek rowdyism and garish dress and shrines to Dionysus and Zeus, that

Phoenician woman had come pleading for the blessings of Jesus upon her daughter. "Send her away," Nathanael and other disciples, too, had protested, "for she crieth after us." No devout man should console these aliens in creed and kind. Shun her! But no, Jesus had turned to her tenderly. "O woman, great is thy faith . . ." And he had assuaged her.

Nathanael tramped wearily on up the hill. Now willows grew in the hollows, and swallows arced from tree to tree. Jesus led them across a defile, toward a wide, gentle incline on the face of the mountain. The throng followed, chattering and sliding and still intoning hymns, "God is our refuge and strength . . ."

It was odd that Jesus exhorted tirelessly and patiently to teach and guide these people, yet would take no practical advantage of it. At times, the crowds had clamored to invest him with the powers of a reigning king. But he would have none of it. He had turned away, dismayed at the notion, and gone alone into the uplands to pray.

". . . whosoever of you will be the chiefest, shall be servant of all. . . ." The riddle of Jesus would not abate. Nathanael's head ached; he did not know if it resulted from the heat and dust, or another cause. "And whosoever shall exalt himself shall be abased; and he that shall humble himself shall be exalted."

Nathanael recalled the day Philip had persuaded him to go to meet this prophet of poor Nazareth. At the time, Nathanael had been in the garden of his house, reading under a fig tree, the place recommended by the rabbis for studying the Torah. Reluctantly he had rolled up the scroll and stepped out to the hedge-lined road.

There he stood, a tall, bearded man, with a sun-browned, angular face, wearing a white robe of woven wool, girded with leather, his clear, discerning eyes watching Nathanael's approach. "Behold an Israelite indeed," Jesus had said, "in whom is no guile!"

Nathanael had caught his breath. "Whence knowest thou me?"

The searching eyes had measured him, comprehended him. Jesus had said gently, ". . . when thou wast under the fig tree, I saw thee."

Before he could stop himself, and without knowing exactly why, the words had burst from Nathanael's lips. "Rabbi, thou art the Son of God . . ." He could not describe even now what had moved him to say it. He did not often speak impulsively, but he had done so then. Standing there in the presence of the man, he had believed.

Jesus had smiled tolerantly. "Because I said unto thee, I saw thee under the fig tree, believest thou?"

It had not been a rational conclusion. Nathanael could not answer the question then, and he could not specifically answer it now. But the conviction had stayed in him, all through their travels to teach and help the distressed in the towns of Galilee; at Capernaum, Magdala, Chorazin, Bethsaida; far north to the mouth of the Jordan at Caesarea Philippi; across eastward to the Greek cities of the Decapolis; southward into Judea and back again; in synagogues and public squares, on mountainsides and seashores.

So now, the carefully schooled, young Nathanael, elegant in temperament, delicate in frame, still toiled among the chosen twelve—with the brawny, blunt fishermen and the muscular, rough-skinned laborers and tradesmen, sharing tasks shoulder to shoulder with these comrades in burlap. And with Jesus. "Blessed are the poor . . . they that mourn . . . the meek . . . the merciful . . . they which are persecuted for righteousness' sake . . ." Challenges to the accepted maxims of the day. "Come unto me, all ye that labour and are heavy laden, and I will give you rest."

The crowd was settling down now on the soft, grassy slope, the women gathering their young, the men squatting or stretching out on the green grass, waiting to hear from the one who broke through their miseries to give them strength and self-respect and hope.

Jesus was talking privately to a man whose wife and children pressed in near him. He, still conversing, casually stroked the tangled hair of a small girl. Out over the gathering, the clamor ebbed, but here and there youngsters still shouted or whimpered, and mothers scurried to quiet them.

With a pang, Nathanael remembered how he and some of the others had tried at first to preserve dignity by rebuffing the children, by keeping the curious little ones away. But that had brought a firm rebuke from Jesus, one of the few times Nathanael had ever seen him show irritation. "Suffer little children to come unto me, and forbid them not . . ." Were there to be no limitations, no aloofness in the rule of Jesus?

Why, he constantly let these women, these mothers charged to keep strictly to their households, bring their young to him, and he cradled them in his arms, and murmured admiringly over them. ". . . of such is the kingdom of God," he would say. ". . . who so shall receive one such little child in my name, receiveth me. . . . Whosoever therefore shall humble himself as this little child, the same is greatest in the kingdom of heaven."

Nathanael sat down, took a linen cloth from the folds of his robe and wiped his neck and face and smoothed his beard. He took a small stick and cleaned his nails. Tidiness was impossible in these roaming pursuits. And so many of the old restraints, which had kept a man protected from his inferiors, no longer seemed valid.

Startlingly, Jesus had even allowed the approach of lepers, wearing those warning bells about their necks, and of a woman with a festered sore. Either defiled him under the law. And when mendicants and madmen wailed for him from the roadsides, he would not let them be silenced, but went to them—hearkening to the afflicted.

At times, when crowds jostled him toward the sea, almost crushing him, Jesus had not been provoked but had merely climbed into a rocking boat to talk from there. Nathanael remembered how on occasions when the throngs were fretful, tired, hungry and far from home, he and others insisted, "Send them away!" But Jesus would not have it. He would tend them, nourish them, and bring them solace.

The master was speaking now, seated there on a mound before the multitude in the customary posture of the Jewish teacher, speaking in his plain Aramaic, in his easy, rural Galilean accent. ". . . whatsoever ye would that men should do to you, do ye even so to them . . . And whosoever shall compel thee to go a mile, go with him twain. Give to him that asketh thee . . . do good to them that hate you, and pray for them which despitefully use you . . . love one another . . ."

The place had become very quiet, except for the deep, resonant voice. Down below, Nathanael could see the Galilee lake, cupped between the hills, shimmering like a huge sapphire sixty furlongs across.

High above, an eagle wheeled, and Nathanael watched the grace of the wheeling. He had, in truth, lost the life he once knew, the prim and prudent isolation of self-honoring appearances, but he had found in Jesus, this sternly compassionate, white-robed friend beside him, a strange, enchanting realm where love soared far and wide, embracing all, and then returned again like the circling yonder of the eagle.

Nathanael, young, intelligent, quick and critical in appraisal, often called Bartholomew or Bar Tolmai—son of Tolmai—had given himself to the unaccustomed way of Jesus, and knew it was good, knew it despite his distractions, knew he would not turn back, knew that with Jesus there were no distinctions, that all humankind, wasted, wounded or abandoned, were equally beloved in his sight. And he knew that a good thing, indeed, had come out of Nazareth.

In the times that followed, Nathanael, like his fellow

apostles, sometimes wavered, blundered and even fled in the fever of dread, but he retained the armor of faith. In the cresting strength of his spirit, he marched on, offering the succor of Jesus to new, oppressed multitudes. Tradition says he died for the cause, that he was flayed, tied in a sack, and thrown into the sea.

9

THE SAMARITAN WOMAN

*"Then cometh he to a city . . . which
is called Sychar . . ."*

SHE TURNED on her back and yawned,
and stretched her limbs. It must be late.
The sun boiled in through the half-open
door. She closed her eyes again, flexing
her toes.

Hours before, while it still was dark, she had heard
the man get up, stir about getting dressed and leave. He
might be back. He might not. She never knew. She
hadn't even let him know she was awake. It worked
easier that way, to keep silent, so there could be no hard
words.

Thank God that part of the day could be consumed
in sleep. You didn't have to live that part. But always
the other hours remained. You had to put up with them.
You couldn't stay locked in that opiate closet all the time,
but you could drag it out as long as possible.

She threw the cover aside and sat up, resting her forehead on her hand for a moment. She ran her tongue around inside her mouth. Too much *shekhar* last night. It left her with a dry, astringent taste. She got up, closed the door and poured herself a cup of water. It went down, tepid and flat. Seated on a little stool, she bathed listlessly, but felt a little better afterward. She picked at some apricots and ate a piece of cheese, scraping off the moldy edges.

She got out her oils and salves. She had to keep up her appearance. What else could she do? There was nothing else left. She rubbed her dark face and breast with palm oil, noticing the blotch on her shoulder. It still felt a little sore. She combed and bound her hair, fixing it with pins, and tied a light blue fillet around it. Opening her perfume, she smiled wanly. If life could only be half so refreshing. . . . She touched her throat, arms and knees with essence of heliotrope, using it sparingly. She had only a few drops left, and didn't know when, if ever, she might get more.

She slipped on her *sadhin*, and over that a blue outer wrapper. It was worn and faded, but the best she had, and she had found that she should always wear her best, even though it wasn't very good. One could never tell. She might meet some new benefactor, if you could call it that.

She dipped a finger in the pigment of antimony to darken her eyebrows and lashes, but then changed her mind. It always made the women glare at her and pull their children aside. Some would anyway. But she wiped her finger clean, leaving her face untinted. It was just as well, considering her plain apparel. She used to own agate necklaces, earrings and brooches, but she had had to sell them.

It must be getting close to the sixth hour, around noon. She always preferred to make her daily trip to fill her water jug about that time. The other women didn't go to the well in the heat of the day, so they would not be there to stare, to draw away from her and whisper.

She picked up the jug and rope and went out, the sunlight hitting her like a cudgel. Her eyelids fluttered against the glassy brightness, and she started off along the dirt street. Not another living thing moved. The whole village of Sychar seemed to be in hiding from the searing noonday.

She took the road that led out to Jacob's well, just a short walk outside of town. The water there always seemed cooler and purer than that of the village wells. Besides, she liked the stroll into the country, away from the houses and shops, away from the snickers, rolled eyes and remarks behind the shutters. Being out there alone was almost as merciful as sleep.

The sun wasn't so bad, once the first shock of it wore off, and she dawdled along, digging her bare feet into the soft sand. She had to keep to the edge of the road where weeds and bushes provided patches of shade to step in. Out in the middle, the sand was so hot it would have kept her jumping or raised blisters.

No matter what other people thought of her, she felt a patriotic pride in the old well out here in the fields. It was a sacred spot, on ground hallowed by Jacob, father of the twelve tribes of Israel. She liked to sit and gaze into its limpid depths. She drew a special comfort from the place, a kind of reverence and sense of goodness. Anyone would laugh at her, thinking that way. But she never mentioned it. She kept it to herself. To her the place had become a sort of private retreat, a secret bower of cleansing and solace.

It was situated on the broad, level plain of Mahneh, about midway between two towering mountains. Mount Ebal, the "mount of cursing," rose just to the north, and on the south, stood the great Mount Gerizim, the "mount of blessing." Here the Samaritans had built their Temple in rivalry with the Jews, but it had been destroyed more than a hundred years ago.

In contrast, the Jews still had their lavish Temple on Mount Zion in Jerusalem. The rancor between the two regions had persisted for nearly ten centuries, going back to the ancient split between southern Judea and northern Israel. Then Jezebel, the Phoenician wife of the northern King Ahab, brought idolatry and dissolute cults into Samaria. Assyrians later seized the land, deported most of its inhabitants (the lost tribes) and settled it with non-Israelites. But the seeds of the old feud took new racial roots, and the darker-skinned Samaritans became the inheritors of Jewish hostility.

To the Jews, the Samaritans were corrupters, perverters, barbarous freebooters—and Jezebels. The Samaritans, in return, looked on the Jews as self-righteous, arrogant pretenders. Most Samaritans, acquiring the national traditions of their predecessors, had accepted belief in the first five books of Moses, but no more. Jews had their long line of other lawgivers and prophetic scriptures.

Out of these elements had grown up a caustic enmity. Jews deemed it dangerous to life and property to pass through Samaria, and usually avoided it. The great trade routes between Egypt and the Far East ran through there, depositing pagan deviations. Among common Jewish expressions were "Thou art a Samaritan and hast a devil" and "He that eats the bread of the Samaritans is like to one that eats the flesh of swine."

Now, under the scorching sun, the Samaritan woman walked along the road toward her favorite sanctum, Jacob's well.

She let the rope drag in the sand, wondering what she would do later in the day. She could go to Shechem, a larger city, not far away. At times she had found someone there interested in her, for a while. She kicked the ground hard with her foot, spraying dirt ahead of her.

If she could change herself, or flee, or begin anew, she would do it. But there was no way. Reforming wouldn't help. The townspeople would never accept her. A man could change, but not a woman. It was even argued whether a woman had a soul. No, she couldn't run away. She had no place to go, no one to whom to go, and no money with which to go alone. Besides, in any place outside Samaria where no one would recognize her, she would be a hated Samaritan. Were it not for that, perhaps she could somehow manage to go to Judea . . . or anywhere. It was no use. She was a Samaritan.

She strolled on indolently, not caring how long it took her, her eyes on the ground to pick the shady spots.

On either side of the road stretched wide, flat fields of ripening barley and wheat. It carpeted the whole valley in sunlit gold.

Glancing up ahead, she stopped short. A man sat on the wellhead. The intruder! Hardly ever before had she seen anyone out here at this time of day. It would spoil her visit to the well. She felt a proprietary tie to the place, and the man had no right usurping it.

She walked on, her expression hardening. She might as well make the best of it. The natural softness of her face tightened into contours partly belligerent, partly imploring—the twin contradictions of her life among other human beings.

But as she drew near, she became puzzled. The man was a stranger. She had never seen him before. From his features, he appeared to be a Jew, and his robe differed from that of a Samaritan. He seemed to be waiting, or resting, as if in the midst of a journey. Certainly, he looked tired. Streaks of muddy sweat disappeared into his beard, and dust coated the white of his pallium and turban. Jews almost never traveled through the country alone, if at all, and most travelers followed the main caravan route through Shechem and the larger towns. Although its grades were steeper, few ever came through these flat, rural plains east of Ebal.

She pulled her scarf about her face and moved on somewhat tensely to the side of the well opposite him. The shaft of the well was seven and a half feet wide, so that she didn't have to come up immediately beside him. Had that been necessary, a Jew might have edged away to keep from being tainted by a Samaritan—even though he didn't know her own reputation. She was glad he didn't know that part. It gave her a rare feeling of dignity.

She kept her eyes averted, tying the ropes on the handles of the waterpot. She lowered it into the water, and the splash made widening ripples on the surface. Even with the man sitting there, she felt a trace of the well's soothing strength as she stared into its azure depths. It went down more than a hundred feet, fed by unfailing springs around its rock walls. The coolness came up and brushed her face. Slowly she drew the filled jug back toward the top.

"Give me to drink."

The rope slipped in her fingers and she nearly lost the whole pot and pulley, but she caught hold again in time and lifted the water back up to the platform, spilling a little on her dress and feet. She was sure now he was a Jew. She could tell by his pronunciation. She eyed him dubiously.

"How is it that thou, being a Jew, askest drink of me, which am a woman of Samaria?" It was inconceivable that a Jew, with their starchy superiority, would do such a thing, but he seemed unimpressed by the question, and she gave it to him squarely, ". . . the Jews have no dealings with the Samaritans."

She thought at first he must have some ulterior motive in mind, because Jews customarily didn't address any strange woman, much less one of her race. But he didn't look that way. He looked disapproving, not of her, but of the idea itself, as if what she had said about the old racial prejudices bespoke an attitude he had rejected.

He shook his head slowly, sighing, and then his eyes came up and rested on her, seeming to examine her personally for the first time. A gentle interest kindled in them, a look of real and kindly concern such as she could not remember receiving from any man . . . from anyone. She dabbled nervously with the rope, untying it from the jar.

"If thou knewest the gift of God, and who it is that saith to thee, Give me to drink; thou wouldest have asked of him, and he would have given thee living water." He spoke compassionately, as if actually wanting to help her, as if he wished to offer her some true service.

But she wouldn't be deceived. She had been misled by soft words too often, even though this man seemed unlike any others she had ever known. There was a tender intimacy in the way he looked at her, and yet it was utterly selfless, as if he had only her welfare at heart, as if he, a stranger, actually cared for her. It was ridiculous, ridiculous. She had too much experience to be taken in by any high-flown offers. He didn't even have a rope. How could he give anyone water of any kind?

"Sir," she said archly, setting the water jug down in front of him with a thump, "thou hast nothing to draw with, and the well is deep: from whence then hast thou that living water?" She paused, watching him lift the jug to his mouth. Then she added another jibe, "Art thou greater than our father Jacob, which gave us the well, and drank thereof himself, and his children, and his cattle?"

The man drank heartily, holding the jug up with both hands, then set it down and turned on her an appreciative smile. "Whosoever drinketh of this water shall thirst again," he said. Droplets clung to his beard. "But whosoever drinketh of the water that I shall give him shall never thirst. [It] shall be in him a well of water springing up into everlasting life." He picked up the rope, knotted it deftly, lowered the jug back into the well and brought it up full for her once more. He sat back down on the wellhead.

She started to leave, but what he had said, or the sincere way he had said it, held her there, as if it contained some remote germ of hope for herself. Yet still she forced a skeptical grin to her lips and turned back toward him. "Sir, give me this water, that I thirst not, neither come hither to draw."

His eyes measured her again, tenderly, understandingly, as she stood there in her faded dress, the defensive grin fixed to her lips, the emptiness and need stabbing through the taut challenge of her face. "Go, call thy husband," he said soberly, "and come hither."

"I have no husband," she flared, biting her lip to stop its trembling.

"Thou hast well said," he agreed. "For thou hast had five husbands; and he whom thou now hast is not thy husband: in that saidst thou truly."

The water jug fell from her hands, and the brilliant noonday seemed to darken and brighten, darken and brighten. She looked down at the wavering pool at her feet, so shallow and fleeting compared to Jacob's well.

How did this man, this foreigner, know about her? She felt shamed and helpless before him now, and yet he neither berated nor condemned her. He only saw her, comprehended her and knew her.

She looked up at him dismally. "Sir, I perceive that thou art a prophet." She spread her hands, questioning, appealing to him, but knowing the thick barrier that separated them. "Our fathers worshipped in this mountain; and ye say, that in Jerusalem is the place where men ought to worship."

He smiled at her encouragingly. ". . . believe me, the hour cometh, when ye shall neither in this mountain, nor yet at Jerusalem, worship the Father." There is no boundary, he said, no fences and distinctions between places and races, between east and west, in God's intent for men. ". . . salvation is of the Jews. But the hour cometh, and now is, when the true worshippers shall worship the Father in spirit and in truth: for the Father seeketh such to worship him."

He seemed to be asking, inviting her, he, a Jew, saying that the Father sought such as her, a Samaritan woman of sordid conduct. The strangeness of her finding him here alone at this well, at this place of her consolation, struck her now with sudden import. "I know," she said tremulously, "that Messias cometh, which is called Christ: when he is come, he will tell us all things."

"I that speak unto thee am he."

Just then a group of men came up the Shechem road to the well, carrying newly purchased provisions. Apparently they were his disciples. Being nearest them, she heard them muttering about why their master should be talking to a strange woman, recalling the rabbinical saying, "A man should hold no conversation with a woman in the street, not even with his own wife, still less with any other woman, lest men should gossip." But none dared question him for it.

She glanced at him, in awe now. He responded with a trusting smile. A spring of hope and usefulness welled in her. She left her waterpot where it lay, and went running toward the village, ignoring the hot sand, her feet flying across it, feeling nothing but the new bloom of purpose within her.

The townspeople had returned to the streets and shops, and with a surging confidence and unabashed candor, she urged them, "Come, see a man, which told me all things that ever I did: is not this the Christ?" They hooted and ogled at first, but she kept at them.

She seemed a different woman, even to herself, no longer slinking and retreating, but hurtled along on a crest of new and momentous faith, facing them all without a quaver, passionately earnest, disarmingly frank, unshakably determined; very soon they stopped hooting, and in a little while they became curious, and then, in a spreading whirl of excitement, practically the whole town turned out to see this purported Christ.

He spoke to them. He taught them. He explained to them. ". . . God sent not his Son into the world to condemn the world; but that the world through him might be saved." He told them of forgiveness and charity, of sustaining the weak and rebuilding the broken. He told them of the great bond that joins all men, Samaritan and Jew, the short and tall, the mighty and the meek, in the fold of God. He perceived that a good Samaritan could be the real neighbor of a Jew, while fellow Jews might pass him by half-dead on the road. Race was no demarcation of love.

Many who dwelt in Sychar heard and believed. They brought others to hear. They begged him to stay in their village, and he tarried for two more days. Many more believed. They went to the Samaritan woman, with neighborly gratitude and new esteem. She herself had convinced many of them at the beginning, and after hearing him, they told her:

"Now we believe, not because of thy saying: for we have heard him ourselves, and know that this is indeed the Christ, the Saviour of the world."

They believed in a Jew who had burst through the centuries of hate and malignance and said he was one of them, and Samaritans one with him; that God was not confined to Mount Zion or Mount Gerizim, but resided in spirit wherever man's heart gave lodging. They believed because a desolate, debased woman, a cheap tramp in their eyes, had first believed, had found in him that wellspring of life she hunted so long at Jacob's well, had believed so forcefully that it turned her into an indefatigable champion of his cause.

So it was that Jesus, when he paused at a well on a hot midday en route between Judea and Galilee, first disclosed his Messiahship to the woman of Samaria. So it was that through her he first proclaimed his mission to the wide world. So it was that this shunned and dishonored Samaritan woman, this creature despised because of her own misspent life, and rejected because of her race, became the first successful woman missionary for Christ.

10

SIMON

*"And one of the Pharisees desired him
that he would eat with him."*

O BE IT. He had committed himself. He would not back out. Simon stood at the front of his house, the fingers of one hand drumming on the burnished doorpost. Jesus would be there that night, and all the town would know. They would see Simon, the impeccable Pharisee, sitting at supper with a non-*habher!* It had been a reckless action for him to send a manservant to call Jesus as a guest to his table, and Simon knew it, but he had done it and he would bear the consequences. Would that all went quietly and without offense.

On several occasions here in Capernaum, Simon had met the man of Nazareth, listened to him speak and rather liked him, despite the disturbing talk about him. But he realized full well that sharing a meal with a nonconformist was regarded by his fellow Pharisees—the *habherim*—as "among the things that shame a pupil" of the law.

Simon straightened his mantle, the flowing black garment of the scholar, and stepped outside. He crossed the open portico and walked slowly down the street, his back erect, his head high, looking neither to right nor to left.

The affair tonight, he knew, could damage his position among the populace. As a Pharisee, as one of the eminently moral and learned separatists who stood apart from the errant rank and file of men, Simon had an honored standing and great public esteem at stake.

Along the street, townspeople bent their heads and greeted him with deference as they passed. Simon nodded absentmindedly. "Peace be unto you. . . . Peace . . ."

After all, he had heard many upsetting and painful reports about Jesus, despite the man's amiability and flair for discernment. It was said he had even suggested that precise knowledge of the elaborate religious codes and compliance with ritual were not fundamental to holiness. A most disruptive notion! But surely the man recognized the safeguarding principle: "Those that knoweth not the law are cursed." Simon compressed his lips. Without such restrictions, ignorance would be made to appear acceptable in God's sight. And imbeciles, with no notion of proper observances, could count themselves good. He snorted. Never! It could not be allowed.

If one were to remain undefiled, the 613 commandments of the Torah must be followed and "interpreted with careful exactitude." These laws, these 365 prohibitions and 248 affirmative rules of work, conduct, eating and worship, constituted the principal test of virtue. Besides, to the five books of Mosaic law, through study, experience and vigilance, the Pharisees had added countless other technical requirements—"made a hedge about the Torah"—to protect the godly from the possibility of coming even close to an infraction. Righteousness thus became a high art. Scholarship was essential to character.

Simon paused at the corner, gazing abstractedly out toward the fish-cutting houses that cluttered the Galilee lakeshore. He would be exceedingly cautious during the evening. He did not want any scandal at his house. Despite the pleasantness of Jesus, the man apparently had a most incisive tongue, a way of gaining mastery when challenged.

In this very town more than a year ago, Jesus had dined at the house of a publican—a spineless customs collector for Rome—along with a number of obvious sinners. Some of the *habherim* had pounced on him, demanding why he ate with "publicans and sinners." It was a firm teaching that, though hospitality to the poor was praiseworthy, a man must "keep far from an evil neighbor and not associate with the wicked," certainly not break bread with them—the symbol of closest comradeship. But Jesus had ingeniously turned the act into a laudable purpose. "They that are whole have no need of the physician," he had said, "but they that are sick: I came not to call the righteous, but sinners to repentance."

A gust of wind hit Simon, and he clutched at his cap, barely catching it. He slapped it severely back on his head and walked on down the street, vexed at the wind—at the winds cutting through his thoughts.

Just south of here, on the plain of Gennesaret, when

Jesus and some of his followers had been eating in the open country without the prescribed ceremonial washings of hands and wrists, watchful Pharisees had called him to account for transgressing the hallowed oral tradition. He had replied coolly, "Why do ye also transgress the commandment of God by your tradition?" Then he had turned to the throng of common people of the land, those unlettered folk who did not even know the minimum amount of water that must be used in the washings, and said, "Hearken unto me . . . There is nothing from without a man, that entering into him can defile him: but the things which come out of him, those are they that defile the man."

Simon, his face clouded, turned abruptly into his net-making shop. The workmen stopped their duties to stare at him. He stood there a moment distractedly, then waved them brusquely back to their work and walked over to the corner stand of records.

This Jesus struck into sensitive questions, he thought. It was true that some of those poor people of the hovels and caves and those with no roofs at all often lacked the wherewithal for the necessary ablutions before meals. The man had a certain sense. Simon picked up the bronze stylus and, dipping it into the dye, began figuring the nets sold here during the week and those transported to the coasts, determining the tenth part of both for tithing. But his thoughts wandered.

The fellow Jesus had a knack of adapting the Pharisees' own astute form of rabbinical debate, countering a question with a question—like the time some of the *hab-*

herim had denounced him at the synagogue here in Capernaum for breaking the Sabbath by mending a stonemason's hand. He had snapped back: "Is it lawful to do good on the sabbath days . . . to save life, or to kill?" On another occasion, when accused of a similar Sabbath violation by helping a man with dropsy, he had retorted: "Which of you shall have an ass or an ox fallen into a pit, and will not straightway pull him out on the sabbath day?"

Simon slammed down the pen, splattering a bit of dye onto the stand. Such observations were difficult to deal with, but law was law, and must not be whittled down, else all be corrupted. Refined ordinances had been evolved to safeguard the Sabbath, and treating the sick, except in dire emergency, was forbidden. The matter of the Sabbath was a delicate thing.

One might bestow alms on the day if a beggar put his hand through the door, but not if the donor had to reach beyond his own threshold. One might ride a burro, but not if one carried a switch—a burden. Travel beyond two-thirds of a mile was prohibited, unless food had been placed the day before at the farthest limit, thereby permitting one to go the distance once over. Scholars in the schools were studying whether a man with a wooden leg should walk on the day since the leg was a burden.

But Jesus and some of his men had even been caught plucking corn in the field on the Sabbath and rubbing out the grain to eat—an undeniable breach of the rule against threshing. He had explained curiously, "The sabbath was made for man, and not man for the sabbath . . ." How presumptuous! To imply that men, however sacred, were above the law!

Simon rolled the records slowly, tightly in his long fingers, thinking. Then he exhaled wearily, shoved the records roughly into the box, and stood up. He glanced about the room, at the workers' hands moving skillfully, tying the woven strands into fishing nets, then spoke briefly to his overseer and left.

Usually he spent a longer period of the day there, but the approaching supper made him restive. He walked back to his large house. As he entered, he noted the shadow on the dial outside the porch. It was nearly time for the afternoon Shema.

A puzzling thing about this man Jesus: Even though he had challenged some of the most pious practices, he declared homage to the ancient Scriptures. "Think not that I am come to destroy the law, or the prophets: I am not come to destroy, but to fulfil . . . Till heaven and earth pass, one jot or one tittle shall in no wise pass from the law, till all be fulfilled."

Simon adjusted the phylacteries on his forehead and left arm—the leathern pieces with the holy inscriptions. He scowled at the slight tremor of his fingers.

In a way, this Jesus seems to have much in common with us, he thought. His saying, "Whatsoever ye would that men should do to you, do ye even so to them," is a firm Pharisaic maxim. So, too, is his stress on doing the will of the "Father which is in heaven." Like him, we seek to win converts, would ". . . compass sea and land to make one proselyte . . ." And he has spurned earthly craftiness and gain, putting goodness above office, being concerned for the poor, for spiritual stature, even as we are.

Perhaps this was why many Pharisees privately admired him, but refrained from professing their admiration openly, wanting to keep the "praise of men" only for their own kind. Moreover, some men had been banished from synagogues for defending him.

At the ninth hour, the time of the afternoon sacrifice at the Temple, Simon draped his head with the prayer shawl and knelt, facing toward Jerusalem, to recite a long prayer. It was a thrice daily practice, at midmorning, noon and midafternoon. When he had finished, he stood up, clapped his hands and instructed his serving women on the meal for that evening. It would be simple and without undue pomp or formality. Simon did not want to give observers the impression of lavish attention to Jesus. Even in plainest style, the occasion was laden with uncertainties.

He went into his bedchamber and carefully combed his fine, full beard. Its projecting corners, in accordance with the law, had never been rounded. The comb slipped from his fingers and fell to the floor. He snatched it up irritably, wondering if his clumsiness today might be an omen of the evening.

He remembered how keenly Jesus had assailed some habits of the Pharisees, saying they make a pretense of long prayer in the streets, that they enlarge their phylacteries and the hems of their garments to appear more devout; that they ". . . love salutations in the marketplaces, and the chief seats in the synagogues . . . Ye are they which justify yourselves before men; but God knoweth your hearts . . .

why beholdest thou the mote that is in thy brother's eye, but considerest not the beam that is in thine own eye?"

For all that, Simon confessed himself curious about the man. He wanted to scrutinize him personally, to put him on display, and judge him. He could not deny he sensed some vague merit in him. The Pharisees themselves had a droll set of descriptions for some of the types he mentioned:

The "shoulder" Pharisee, who wore his good deeds on his shoulder and obeyed precepts not by principle but by expedient.

The "wait a little" Pharisee, who pleaded he needed more time before he could do the right thing.

The "painted" Pharisee, who advertised his holiness lest anyone touch or contaminate him.

The "reckoning" Pharisee, who managed to devise some lesser duty to take the place of a hard duty.

But most of them, Simon thought stubbornly, were true Pharisees "of love." He drew back his shoulders, lifted his head and stepped back out into the large hall with its flagstone floor. He folded his arms and stood there, absently watching the women at their work, proud of the tradition he represented.

The Pharisees, Simon reminded himself, were philosophical descendants of the heroic Maccabean brothers, who had fought off Syria's enforced heathenism and cleansed the Temple of its idol to the Greek god, Zeus. Courageous and undeviating in their faith, deeply respected, they had refused any compromise with pagan overlords. Thousands were slain by the successors of

the Macedonian invader, Alexander, because of their un-
swerving convictions. In contrast, the landed, power-
minded Sadducees ignored religion and concentrated on
political manipulation. They accepted almost any gross
device to keep control of the profitable priesthood and the
local Jewish governments under Rome's dominion. But
not the Pharisees—not the unsullied separatists who stood
aloof in their holiness and intellect from the tainted masses
and who referred only to each other as *habherim*—"neighbor." Most were ordinary city artisans or teachers, but
they were an elite in their piety.

Even the habit of praying in public had once required
valor back when the Pharisees started it during the persecutions of Antiochus IV. Many then had been tortured for
displaying their faith. And now they still continued the
practice, even though shorn of its moral worth. It helped
hold public respect for their sanctity.

Simon strolled across the room, rubbing at the dull
ache in the back of his neck. Undeniably, Jesus had let fly
at the Pharisees. Perhaps because of their zeal in trying to
discredit him. Perhaps because he felt some need to show
his difference from them. Certainly, his difference from
the worldly, rich Sadducees already was clearly manifest.
There was no need to point that out.

At length Simon returned to the front of the house
and stood on the porch, watching the sun sink. Some
pupils came for their lessons, but he curtly sent them away,
not even noticing which ones they were; for a whole series
of episodes involving Jesus troubled his mind, and he
looked ahead to the meal with increasing discomfiture.

Each time, the man had emerged undiminished. Simon could visualize the barbed questioning of critics, then the tense stillness among the listeners, followed by Jesus' level, penetrating replies.

Simon took a long breath. The sun had gone down. He went back into the house and sat down in his bed-chamber, waiting in the dark. Through the doorway, he could see the trembling lamplight, and spears of it stabbed eerily across the floor toward him. A servant came and said the guests were arriving.

Jesus was at the door. Simon stood there stiffly while his guest set his staff against the wall and removed his sandals. Simon did not extend any of the special courtesies —no welcoming kiss, no water for a foot bath, no anoint-ment of the hair. A few of Simon's intimates also had ar-rived on the portico, and he turned his attention to them. He did not want to cause gossip or embarrassment by showing special honor to Jesus.

They reclined on the couches about the table, and after the water had been poured over their hands and they had dried them and prayed, they began to eat. For a time there was little conversation. Simon spoke of casual mat-ters to his friends. He sensed they, too, were under a strain, with the non-*habber* in their midst. Jesus ate, com-plimenting the host on the victuals, seeming wholly at ease.

Just as Simon had feared, a number of townspeople wandered into the hall to watch and listen. This was not unusual at such a function. Some were lowly folk, evident wrongdoers.

Then to Simon's shock and dismay, a degraded

woman of the streets, a known prostitute with her hair uncovered, uncoiled and hanging shamelessly down her back, moved in close to the couches. She carried an alabaster box, of the kind that contained ointment. She knelt suddenly beside Jesus, weeping, and began washing his feet with her tears, wiping them with her hair, kissing them.

Simon gagged on the food, coughing, overcome with mortification. No one spoke. Simon felt duty-bound to order the woman away, but Jesus made no complaint, and Simon did not want to cause a hubbub of contention. He thought disparagingly: This man, if he were a prophet, would have known who and what manner of woman this is that toucheth him: for she is a sinner. No prophet, no clean man, would have permitted himself to be so defiled. Simon averted his eyes, hardly able to contain himself, his face red. He was jolted when Jesus spoke:

"Simon, I have somewhat to say unto thee."

Simon swallowed hard. ". . . say on."

Then Jesus began telling a story of two debtors, one who owed five hundred denarii ($100), and the other who owed fifty denarii ($10). Neither could pay, but their creditor canceled both debts. "Tell me therefore," Jesus said, "which of them will love him most?"

Simon squirmed, wondering where the unrelated discussion was leading. "I suppose that he, to whom he forgave most."

"Thou hast rightly judged." Then Jesus turned toward the woman. "[Simon,] Seest thou this woman?"

Yes, yes, of course, he had seen her, had been sure

he had seen her more fully than Jesus had, and had pitied him for his stupidity in not knowing her. But Simon sat mute, feeling denuded, at a loss for an answer.

"I entered into thine house," Jesus went on mildly, "thou gavest me no water for my feet: but she hath washed my feet with tears, and wiped them with the hairs of her head. Thou gavest me no kiss: but this woman since the time I came in hath not ceased to kiss my feet. My head with oil thou didst not anoint: but this woman hath anointed my feet with ointment. Wherefore I say unto thee, Her sins, which are many, are forgiven; for she loved much: but to whom little is forgiven, the same loveth little."

He paused, his gaze traveling slowly around the table, steady, benign, but undeceived. Then he leaned toward the woman and said, "Thy sins are forgiven."

A stunned silence settled over the room. Then the whispers began, the indignant glances, the muffled, horrified words passed from man to man. Who is this that forgives sins? Unspeakable! A sacrilege! Simon sat there, tight-lipped, troubled, his face white now.

Jesus watched them a moment, then turned again to the woman. "Thy faith hath saved thee; go in peace."

He remained there a moment thoughtfully. Then quietly, a little regretfully, he got up, went to the door and picked up his sandals and staff, and walked off barefoot into the night. The people followed after him. The men of the *habherim*, clean, faultless, too good for the people, were left alone in their isolation.

11

MARTHA

*". . . and a certain woman named Martha
received him into her house."*

BAP-BAP-BAP-BAP. Martha held the knife
by both ends, and her hands made swift,
chopping motions as she sheared the olives
into bits. She raked them into a bowl
and quickly began peeling the boiled eggs. A lock
of hair fell over her eyes, and she swept it aside with the
back of her hand, not pausing to tighten the roll. There
was too much to do; there was always too much to do.

A maidservant came in with the platter of hot loaves.
Martha paused to prick them with a sliver. A little over-
browned, she thought, but they would do. Bring the
wine from the storehouse, she told the girl. Martha turned
back to the eggs, stirring them in with the olives, pouring
in careful portions of oil, mashing and whipping the
ingredients together.

Not too many condiments. The rabbis cautioned

against that. Jesus might notice. The roebuck, the roe-buck! It should be finished. She started outside, then caught herself, whirled and went into the bedchamber, grabbed up a looking glass and recoiled her hair. She whisked her widow's veil back over her head and scurried into the court.

Vai L'kidra! Woe to the pot! Her one manservant now sat on the ground completely at his ease, leisurely turning the quarter of roebuck on the spit, not even keeping watch on the other charcoal brazier where the vegetables bubbled and steamed. She rushed over to him. He jumped up. It still lacks a mite, he said. She examined it. Oh, very well. But he must get the serving board put up straightway.

She turned about, swiftly surveying the yard. At least the festival booths looked inviting this year. Jesus and some lesser guests sat in the large, main booth, a rectangular leafy bower open on one side. Martha's younger sister Mary, as usual, was curled up at his feet, listening to him intently. That girl! She should be helping with the supper. Every time Jesus came, Mary got this way. Absolutely useless, captivated by him, following him about, showing him a new bird's nest or flower, nodding eagerly at his words.

Martha turned sharply to the other fire, snatched up the tongs and lifted off the cooking pots of lentils and corn. Certainly both she and Mary adored and respected Jesus. But the girl ought to do a few things to help provide for his needs. Like any useful woman!

Quite often, Jesus had visited them, resting a few days

from his journeys at their house in Bethany just outside Jerusalem, spending the evenings chatting, telling stories of men and places, while Martha bustled about bringing cheeses, cakes, an extra cushion. She always did her utmost to give him comfort and good food. He so seldom had them. And on this present occasion, at the Feast of the Tabernacles, she wanted everything especially pleasant for him.

There had been so much to do beforehand, the supervising of servants in setting up the fresh outdoor booths of living boughs, covered over with leafy branches as specified for use during the week-long autumn festival of harvest, the moving of mattresses, couches and table into the outside quarters. And work aplenty still remained. But Mary! All she could do was to hang at his side, venturing questions, her face alight to his every utterance. Of course, Mary always had been a quiet, meditative girl, wandering about the grove, studying a chameleon, or just sitting, chin in hands, her gaze far away. She should be more practical!

Martha hastened back into the scullery and sent the maidservant after the simmering vegetables. The meal should begin—soon. Always at a hectic time like this, that old adage buzzed in Martha's mind, "To excite the appetite, show the dishes by daylight." She started to open the wine bottles. *Al Tzavarii!* Upon my neck! The wrong ones. She dashed back out to the storehouse, reminding herself that the courtyard lamps must be filled. She fumbled in the dusky interior, finding the special red wine of Sharon she had saved for this day.

Back outside, she noticed that a branch had dropped

from one of the small festival sleeping lodges. She called the manservant, watching impatiently as he made the repairs. Isn't the meat ready? Yes, almost. Then stoke the coals to keep it warm. And set up the board. And fill the lamps. Light them!

She raced toward the house. Sunset rays, slanting through the treetops, made dark ripples on her harried face. Back inside, she began mixing the wine, adding two logs of water for each log of wine. Prepare the washing basins, she told the maid. Martha arranged the wine cups and began filling them. Her brow glistened with perspiration, and her mind reeled.

She still had to mix the spiced wine for after the meal. What if her brother Lazarus came back from the city, bringing other guests? There just wouldn't be places for them. That was all! She already felt overtaxed with the serving to be done. The preserved apricots! They must be fetched!

Martha took the platter of beaten eggs and a platter of loaves and started out the door. The sideboard still was not up. She laid down the platters and hurried outside, calling the manservant, advising him as he adjusted the boards on the supports, her thoughts racing. "To excite ... by daylight." There must also be water, water on the table. Water and salt.

Martha scuttled back into the house, grabbed up the platters, telling the maidservant to bring the basins, dipper and towels. She placed the light course on the board, while Jesus and the guests washed their right hands over the basins. Mary still sat there! Martha's nerves jangled.

She rushed back inside, seized the tray of wine cups. She came first in honor to Jesus, serving him. She felt frayed and on the edge of endurance. Agitatedly, she drew him aside, complaining, "Lord, dost thou not care that my sister hath left me to serve alone? bid her therefore that she help me."

Jesus took the cup, turning it slowly in his fingers. "Martha," he said, and his eyes rested on her fondly, appealingly, "Martha, thou art careful and troubled about many things . . ." He paused, turning the cup again.

Yes, Martha thought, so many things. So many things that there was hardly time to think, or see or wonder. So many troubling things engrossed her that she could scarcely notice anything else. Jesus looked at her again, grateful to her, understanding, yet also with an expression that seemed to say it all wasn't necessary, that all the strain and elaborate hospitality weren't needed, that simple fare was adequate, that there was some other response he valued even more.

"But one thing is needful," he said gently, "and Mary hath chosen that good part, which shall not be taken away from her."

Martha blinked, confused. She moved on, serving the wine, her thoughts momentarily blunted. Jesus spoke the blessing, and she stood there, feeling slightly jarred but also wondering exactly what he meant. Hadn't she been driving herself dizzy, and all for him? Apparently he didn't want her to do that. Well . . .

She placed the loaves and eggs mechanically on the table while the guests stretched on the couches. Oddly, she didn't feel compelled to rush and fret about any longer. Perhaps, she admitted, because she was a little peeved. But it seemed rather good, slowing down to a more even, natural pace, to a calmer mood. She sighed, actually relieved in a sense. The maidservant appeared with the basins for the washing of both hands—without even being told! Jesus blessed the bread, and Martha now found herself pausing to listen. They began to eat.

It was curious. All the harassing annoyances of a while ago didn't seem so urgent any more. In fact, what were they? Martha went about the rest of her duties, efficiently but strangely subdued. She scarcely spoke a single order to the servants, but somehow everything went smoothly and easily. The main dishes were served and later the fig cakes and apricots and the final wine flavored with honey and pepper—even leaving time on her hands. Puzzled, she went out and sat down with Mary at his side. She felt relaxed, her mind clear, for the first time all evening. How pleasant.

But she could not refrain from bestirring herself to adjust that cushion properly at Jesus' shoulder. After all!

After the festival week of Tishri 15 to 22, during which Jesus met stoning threats while preaching in close-by Jerusalem, he left with his disciples for Galilee, and Martha watched them go regretfully. She and her sister would miss him. But they didn't know how much. They didn't know that when they saw him again not many months later, they themselves would be in deep personal distress.

Poor Jesus, Martha thought. He seldom had the proper comforts of home, except here, always going from place to place, teaching, helping, with no sure haven for the night, pressing tirelessly on. It worried her. Once he had said, "The foxes have holes, and the birds of the air have nests, but the Son of man hath not where to lay his head." But he didn't complain. He said a fuller glory in life consisted of something else, not practical or even sensible by ordinary standards, but lovelier by far. What were those words of his that Mary repeated?

"Take no thought for your life, what ye shall eat, or what ye shall drink . . . Is not the life more than meat, and the body than raiment? . . . seek ye first the kingdom of God . . . and all these things shall be added unto you. . . . Behold the fowls of the air: for they sow not, neither do they reap . . . Consider the lilies how they grow: they toil not, they spin not; and yet I say unto you, that Solomon in all his glory was not arrayed like one of these."

What was this beauty, surpassing practical workaday burdens?

Perhaps, Martha thought, it was partly what he meant when he said her social exertions choked out what really counted; that one could get so enmeshed in the clutter, so mired in details and irritations that the finer things were missed. Truly, the other things were important. They were what made the cares worth while.

It was strange, she thought, the profound tie she felt to Jesus. And Mary, too. But then Jesus had always been sympathetic toward women, protesting the way they were treated like chattels, with a man able to divorce a wife merely by signing a statement saying, "I . . . do divorce, set free and repudiate you . . ." Jesus maintained that God made male and female to "be one flesh," and "What therefore God hath joined together, let not man put asunder." Yet he didn't expound legalisms, like the Pharisees, but unleashed living principles testifying to the worth of each human being, including women. Perhaps they, too, could dream beyond the pot and pestle.

At the midwinter Feast of Dedication, Jesus again visited Jerusalem. About two months later, Lazarus, the brother of the two sisters in Bethany, became deathly sick. Martha, quick to act and practical, sent a messenger to summon Jesus. He had gone into seclusion at Bethabara, north of the Dead Sea, after encountering keener official antagonism in Jerusalem. It was about thirty miles away, a full day's journey. He could help if anyone could help. But it was no use. Lazarus, whom Jesus loved as he did the sisters, died the next day.

The mourners came and marched behind his body, lamenting, as they carried him to the cavern tomb. It was sealed with a stone. Martha left Mary weeping there and, fighting to control herself, walked back along the file of mourners, numb to their words, "May the Lord of consolation comfort you." If Jesus had only come . . . if he had only been there in time. . . .

But three more days went by. Time and again, Martha stole up the path to the rise, where she could see beyond the trees to the Jericho road, still longing and praying to see his tall figure come in sight. Logically, she knew it no longer mattered. But even now, if he were just here. . . .

Minutes later, as she sat stonily in the chamber of mourning with its overturned chairs and couches as signs of sorrow, a neighbor came and whispered in her ear. Martha's face broke then, and tears slid down her cheeks. She slipped out quietly, suppressing her haste, and went out the gate and up the path again.

He came striding on, at his long, steady gait, his staff and feet raising a little pool of dust around him. Martha wiped her eyes, summoning up all her composure. She wanted to run, but held herself back. They met in the path and kissed. For all her efforts, her voice quavered. "Lord, if thou hadst been here, my brother had not died." She searched for something else to say, knowing nothing could be done, but that somehow whatever he did would be right. "But I know, that even now, whatsoever thou wilt ask of God, God will give it thee."

Lines of fatigue creased Jesus' face. "Thy brother shall rise again."

"I know," Martha said dismally, unrelieved by the thought, ". . . he shall rise again in the resurrection at the last day."

Slowly, patiently, he sought to make it clear. "I am the resurrection, and the life: he that believeth in me, though he were dead, yet shall he live: and whosoever liveth and believeth in me shall never die. Believest thou this?"

Martha nodded hesitantly. "Yea, Lord." She tried to see. She couldn't rationalize it. It wasn't practical. But she wanted to see. "I believe that thou art the Christ, the Son of God, which should come into the world."

Jesus asked her to call Mary. Martha turned forlornly back to the house, leaving him standing by a tree, his head bowed. She went to her sister, and with no word to the others, told her, "The Master is come, and calleth for thee."

Mary's head flew up, her reddened eyes wide and glinting suddenly with hope, and she was on her feet, dashing barefoot across the sticks and leaves. She threw herself on the ground at his feet, and buried her face there. "Lord, if thou hadst been here," she gasped brokenly, "my brother had not died."

Jesus bent over her, his face torn with anguish. A moan rose in his throat. "Where have ye laid him?"

Mary didn't reply, her misery drowned in sobs at his feet.

Jesus wept.

In the tense stillness of the road there, with the Mary and the Martha he loved torn by the tragedy of death, with the pain of humanity at his feet, with the treachery of the world fast closing around his own life, and his role in it only hazily understood, Jesus gave in to weeping.

One of the mourners led him through the trees to the tomb. They stopped and he said quietly, "Take ye away the stone."

Martha winced. "Lord," she protested weakly, "by this time he stinketh: for he hath been dead four days." But they kept pushing at the stone, and then the entrance gaped dark as death itself.

Jesus lifted his head, his eyes on the heavens, his countenance marked by inner struggle. "Father, I thank thee that thou hast heard me." He lowered his head. In a loud, booming voice, he cried, "Lazarus, come forth."

Martha stiffened. A hush hung over them. Then, in the awful quiet, Lazarus came walking out, his arms and legs still wrapped with shrouds.

"Loose him," Jesus said, "and let him go."

No, it didn't make sense. It was like the lilies, a stunning eloquence that outdistanced man's calculations, that leapt even the boundaries of life and death. Martha, sobbing joyously, knew now what Jesus meant, even if it didn't seem reasonable, even if it wasn't practical. She could read the secret of eternity unfolded in one striking event that proclaimed those things which "Eye hath not seen, nor ear heard, neither have entered into the heart of man . . ."

Jesus left the next day. The thread of his time ran short. He trekked across the open fields northward, parallel to the plateau road but avoiding it to prevent seizure, to the little town of Ephraim, nestling at the foot of a thousand-foot drop. A steep, rocky footpath led down to it. Not long afterward, on Nisan 8 of the spring of about 28 A.D., six days before Passover, Jesus came back to Bethany. A supper was given in his honor. Lazarus was there. And contemplative Mary, in a burst of overflowing emotion, anointed his hair with costly spikenard. And practical Martha, knowing now that obsession with everyday affairs can obscure the meaning of life, again served, not with her old distraction, but with calm, loving concern.

So, in their differing ways, the two sisters gave their devotion. With this loyal pair of Bethany Jesus spent many of his last hours on earth—before he died and did for the world what he had revealed in Lazarus.

12

THOMAS

"Behold, we go up to Jerusalem . . ."

HEY HAVE OUTDONE US, Thomas thought. They have come at us from every side and driven us out. Our Master has offered the hand of mercy, and they have replied with stones. We are backed to the wall. The rods of the earth press against us.

Thomas sat cross-legged on the ground, his gaze fastened on the glowing coals. Around the fire were Jesus and the other members of their little group. They spoke little, and when they did, it was only in chopped phrases, in wooden monotones. At length, Jesus got to his feet, and they all looked up at him, starting to rise, too. But he lifted his hand, bidding them stay. He was going apart for a while to pray. He would return soon. His eyes rested on them confidently a moment. Then he walked off in the darkness.

The heavy stillness stole back over them. Thomas

was a contemplative man, a care-worn carpenter whom Jesus called "Didymus," his twin. He worried greatly over any setbacks, but he was sturdy, and he looked at hard facts squarely. He picked up a stick and, reaching out with it, poked at the coals, convinced that the threads of their endeavor were running out. Harassed, threatened, they had come here to this remote region of Bethabara, north of the Dead Sea, and the way back was fraught with peril.

We will go back, nonetheless, Thomas said to himself. We shall walk again in their midst, and the people will come to him and be gathered up and restored by his words—but so, too, will come the destroyers and the haters, and they will take him, and it will be the end. Thomas probed at the coals, and a little flame sprang up, casting its flickering light over the bleak faces of the others, the shadows playing on the bamboo lean-to where some of them sheltered.

Borne down by the huge realities, the brooding Thomas pondered their plight. There is no escaping, he thought. The axe is poised and the tree is marked for the stroke. We have seen the glint of the blade, and its brandishing all about us, in many places, at many times, and the blow cannot but fall upon us.

Some of the disciples got to their feet and walked about restively. None of them would sleep, not until Jesus returned to tell them his plans. The embers burned low.

Even from the first, Thomas had sensed the danger, had heard the low undertones of the world's vengeance. Jesus had said it would be a precarious way. He had not deceived or coddled them. They all should have known it.

On a night more than two years ago, he had led them apart from the crowds into the mountains near Bethsaida, where the Jordan empties into the lake. He led them into a dark and quiet defile and sat down on a stone, and they seated themselves in front of him. Thomas remembered he could hardly see Jesus' face, only the white of his robe, and hear his voice low in the darkness.

". . . I send you forth," he told them, "as sheep in the midst of wolves: be ye therefore wise as serpents, and harmless as doves." They were engaged in a kind of war, Thomas knew then, their shield, wisdom, their weapon, love. Would that be enough? For they battled for the world, and they were only twelve.

"If any man will come after me, let him deny himself, and take up his cross daily, and follow me," Jesus said. "For whosoever will save his life shall lose it: but whosoever will lose his life for my sake, the same shall save it."

Thomas had glanced about at the other disciples, but none of them stirred, none protested, none wanted to quit.

"What I tell you in darkness," Jesus went on, "that speak ye in light . . . that preach ye upon the housetops."

Then, in that secluded council, with clouds covering the moon, his instructions came crisp, direct and urgent:

Take no silver, script or bread, not even a change of garment. Only your staff. In this task, there is no place for ordinary concerns. Eat and lodge wherever the door is open to you. No time can be wasted. The ramparts must be raised before the siege. If a town spurns you, quit it. ". . . shake off the dust of your feet." Do not pause because of reverses. Press on.

"But beware . . ." Jesus said. Enemies will surround you. They will ridicule and scourge you and drag you before their councils. ". . . ye shall be hated . . . for my name's sake: but he that endureth to the end shall be saved."

Far off, Thomas had heard the low mutter of thunder. ". . . fear not them which kill the body, but are not able to kill the soul . . ."

When he had concluded, some of the disciples re- acted with enthusiasm, as if avid for the adventure. They went about regaling each other about the prospects, their chests out, their voices plucky. But Thomas had not shared their optimism. He had remained there on the ground, dread images filing through his mind. Some of the others had twitted him for his dolor. Why so woe- begone, Thomas?

As a carpenter, Thomas knew that you could not judge a tree until you cut into it and examined the grain. In the same way, he looked at men and events. Let reality make its gash; then he would know how firm the fiber. Already, he knew the quality of his Master, his Lord, and was consecrated to him wholeheartedly. But what about himself? The others? In his dogged personal honesty, Thomas feared what might come. He saw the darker portents. He did not hang back, but he also did not count on victory before it was won. Unlike some of the others, he never boasted of his hardihood, never quibbled about rewards, then or later, never pushed for position or favors.

But he trudged along, a muscular, heavy man, with worry chiseled in every lineament.

At the very start of their work, they received a shocking message—perhaps it was an omen, Thomas thought. The king had killed John the Baptist. The rulers of the world had served notice, and the notice was death. Grieving, his disciples had tramped southward to the fortress prison by the Dead Sea and claimed the Baptist's body and buried him there by the Jordan where he used to preach. That was how it had begun—with death. That was the enemy encamped around them. That was the face of the foe. Its portents came from many places, at many times. During those early days around the lake, the Pharisees came to say that Herod Antipas, having taken the Baptist's head, now would slay Jesus. Thomas turned dismally toward the Master, but Jesus shrugged them off. There was work to do. "Go ye, and tell that fox . . . I must walk to day, and to morrow, and the day following . . ."

So they walked, Thomas and the other eleven and Jesus, and the multitudes grew, and the hired hecklers came to hurl their insults. "Friend of sinners!" "Beelzebub!" "Son of the carpenter!" "He . . . is mad; why hear ye him?" Each taunt deepened the creases in Thomas' face. He turned a stick in his hand, its surface worn smooth by his rough fingers.

Jesus remained undeterred, his voice flowing calm and firm, explaining to them, showing them, simply and patiently. This only inflamed the destroyers. When Jesus aided a helpless man on the Sabbath, they called him a lawbreaker, communed how to kill him, and hissed,

"Prince of devils!" He became angry then. ". . . every tree is known by his own fruit." He stood there, seeming to tower over them. And they let him be.

Thomas could not see how they could go on, amid the gathering, unspent fury, but they went on nonetheless, and Jesus impressed upon them the urgency of their work, that all else must be subordinated to its significance. A recruit wanted to go home to a funeral. "Follow me," Jesus said. ". . . let the dead bury their dead." Another wanted to bid his parents farewell. "No man," Jesus said, "having put his hand to the plow, and looking back, is fit for the kingdom of God."

At times Thomas felt as if he were caught in the center of a forest whipped by gales, and no matter what direction they turned, great branches would come crashing down upon them, and lightning would rend the ground beneath their feet. He revolved the stick in his hand, worrying.

"Think not," Jesus said, "that I am come to send peace on earth: I came not to send peace, but a sword." It was a different kind of sword, to be sure, the kind that cuts men off from former attachments, from vainglory and gold and indifference. Thomas felt its cutting force around them.

Jesus, as if from old knowledge, seemed to foresee each step and paced their moves, timed them to his purpose. "Tell no man," he charged new followers at times. "Neither go into the town, nor tell it to any in the town." He seemed able to gauge the weight of hostility, and fit it to his goal. ". . . what king," he said, "going to make

war against another king, sitteth not down first, and con-
sulteth whether he be able with ten thousand to meet him
that cometh against him with twenty thousand?"

But the odds against them were far greater than that,
and Thomas noticed that some of the others now grew
uneasy. After a tense skirmish with hecklers on the Gennesaret plain, one of them warned Jesus, "Knowest thou
that the Pharisees were offended . . . ? "

Ignore it, Jesus said. "Let them alone: they be blind
leaders of the blind. And if the blind lead the blind, both
shall fall into the ditch."

So they went on, and the attackers brought up new
weapons. Squads of ruffians came with the religious rulers,
and they came with armfuls of stones. This happened
more and more often, and Jesus would face them, unflinch-
ing, and look at them, look at them in their sickness, and
their resolution would fail them. Thomas began to realize
that he walked beside a courage he had never known before, that Jesus was unbendable, unbreakable, the true
brave. Nevertheless, he could be killed, and the knowledge hung on Thomas like chains.

There was that time at the Pool of Bethesda, just
outside the Sheep Gate of Jerusalem. Jesus was kneeling
over a sick pauper. They came toward him, picking up
stones as they came. They swaggered up to him, sputter-
ing accusations. Jesus rose, and his eyes swept them like
a command. "My Father worketh hitherto, and I work."
They hesitated, rooted there by their incomprehension.
". . . I seek . . . the will of the Father which hath sent
me," Jesus said.

He turned abruptly and left them, moving unhurriedly along the pillared portico beside the pool. To Thomas, it seemed danger had reached a breaking point, yet it went on, stretching out to a hair's fineness.

". . . Why go ye about to kill me?," Jesus said to the vigilantes who came to seize him as he spoke in the Treasury court of the Temple. "Yet a little while am I with you, and then I go unto him that sent me. Ye shall seek me, and shall not find me . . ."

The religious chiefs in the room harangued against him, and the people whispered among themselves, "Whither will he go . . .? He is a good man. . . . Nay; but he deceiveth the people. . . . How knoweth this man letters, having never learned? . . . this is the very Christ . . . Is not this he, whom they seek to kill? But, lo, he speaketh boldly . . ."

Thomas saw the assassins moving into the room with their stones, and his fingers tightened, twisting the ever-present stick. Jesus spoke on, clearly, positively. Thomas rushed to a priest, asking him to bring guards to prevent bloodshed, but the priest smiled, saying it was none of his affair.

Jesus was still speaking. "My doctrine is not mine, but his that sent me. . . . he that sent me is true . . ." The agitators shuffled about, glancing at one another, cradling their stones, studying the mood of the crowd. "Thou hast a devil . . ." one shouted. Jesus' gaze whipped to him, and the man seemed to shrink beneath the bobbing heads.

". . . I lay down my life . . . No man taketh it from me . . ." Jesus paused, eying the men with stones. ". . . I lay it down of myself. I have power to lay it down, and I have power to take it again. . . ."

They were afraid of him, or confounded, or bloodless before the crowd, and they did not take him that week of the Feast of the Tabernacles. His time had not yet come, he said. Yet Thomas knew they would try again.

It was in the winter, and Jesus spoke on the long, shaded King Solomon's porch on the east side of the Temple. It was Khislev 25, the Feast of the Dedication, in memory of the ousting of idol worship from the Temple two centuries before. Jesus spoke gravely to the pilgrims.

"I am the door: by me if any man enter in, he shall be saved . . . I am come that they might have life, and that they might have it more abundantly. . . ."

Thomas stood there on the porch, his doleful eyes roving over the Kidron valley with the tree-covered Mount of Olives beyond. "I am the good shepherd, and know my sheep . . . As the Father knoweth me, even so know I the Father: and I lay down my life for the sheep. . . . and there shall be one fold, and one shepherd. . . ."

A strident voice broke in. "If thou be the Christ, tell us plainly." Thomas saw them then, the party of bare-armed hirelings, the clutched stones. "I told you, and ye believed not . . . I and my Father are one. . . . Many good works have I shewed you from my Father; for which of those works do ye stone me?"

". . . for blasphemy."

There was a stir and a milling, and Jesus stood there, unruffled. "If I do not the works of my Father, believe me not," he flung at them. "But if I do, though ye believe not me, believe the works . . ." They pressed toward him then, and Thomas thought the end had come, but the crush of listeners surrounded Jesus, and when it had dispersed, Jesus was gone, and the killers stood there with their rocks unthrown.

So now they had withdrawn to this isolated mountain country, and had remained here several weeks. But Jesus said he was needed once more in Judea, and Thomas knew, with a fateful hopelessness, that the Master would go.

Thomas gazed sadly at the other disciples, some of them standing, some sitting by the fire. He wondered if they would be so eager this time, as they once had been. They too must realize that the lines were drawn, the preliminary sallies over, the powers fully aroused and ready to strike. Thomas stirred the fire again, working up a flame. Then he broke the stick, tossed most of it into the fire. He held a short piece in one hand, turning it over and over until the bark peeled and it turned smooth and moist in his grasp. He knew now that Jesus possessed an unshakable valor, that he dwelt on some high plateau of the undaunted. But he also sensed that the Master had reached a limit, that if he went back, he would die.

In a little while, Jesus returned to the fireside and stood there while the disciples gathered around. They came quickly, their movements constrained and hushed. Jesus waited until they were settled. Their faces turned upward toward him, pale in the firelight.

"Let us go into Judaea again," Jesus said.

Thomas had known he would say it, but it seemed to

drop like a stone among the others. None of them spoke for a moment. Their gaze slowly came back down and fixed hard on the fire. Off to one side, someone tossed a pebble into the coals. It bounded off a faggot, spewing up a cone of sparks. As if that had broken some inner dam, the others began shifting about, changing their postures, still not saying anything, but mumbling to themselves, casting stricken looks at each other, waiting for someone to voice their attitude. Thomas turned the stick slowly, tightly, in his fingers. Finally several of the others began speaking at once, complaining in a roundabout way, then more directly, embarrassed by their own trepidations.

"Master," they said, "the Jews of late sought to stone thee; and goest thou thither again?"

"Are there not twelve hours in the day?" Jesus answered. "If any man walk in the day, he stumbleth not, because he seeth the light of this world."

The others remained unassured, even by the Master. They hemmed and hawed, offering excuses why they need not go, suggesting it would be just as well to stay longer in this obscure place, safe from the glare of humanity. ". . . if a man walk in the night," Jesus said, "he stumbleth, because there is no light in him."

Still they hesitated and hedged. Thomas gave the stick a vicious twist in his fingers. It broke with a loud snap. The gloomy, rueful carpenter, who never glossed over the rugged facts, stood up and looked around him challengingly.

"Let us also go," he said, "that we may die with him."

There was no more hesitation.

Neither Thomas nor the others fulfilled this severe challenge at once. They were not intended to. They still had work to do, more days of peril in which to walk, and they girded themselves as men, as the sad-eyed, tough-minded Thomas had done back there on the border line of battle.

Some call him "doubting Thomas," but his were never wanton doubts, only shredded hopes, and a downcast heart, and in the end, he would, in effect, die as he had foreseen—with Jesus. For in furthering the work of his Master, tradition says, Thomas eventually was led to a hill outside the city of Mazdai, in India, where four soldiers ran him through with spears. It could not have been a surprise to Thomas, who never dodged the facts, no matter how depressing, who never adulterated reality to ease his worries or bolster himself up, who looked at the world just as it was, and in doing so found the courage to meet it.

13

ZACCHEUS

". . . there was a man . . . which was the chief among the publicans . . . And he sought to see Jesus . . ."

WITH A SWEEP of his arm, Zaccheus sent the silver bowl flying. It bounced off the woven hangings and spun across the floor amid the spilled fruit and lay there vibrating. Zaccheus stared at it out of dull eyes. The bowl gradually became still, but his eyes stayed on it. The flesh of his pudgy cheeks hung slack and heavy. Finally he turned away, repelled at his own outburst.

The silence returned. It came back like an invisible presence in his great house. It was always there, hovering about the main hall, gliding through his private chambers, stalking the accounting rooms, following him across the rich carpets under foot. He could not escape it. It met him at the table in the morning and lay wakefully beside him on his bed at night. It followed him into the streets and closed the lips of those he met and made them turn away from him. It was his grim doorkeeper.

Zaccheus, a chunky, ungainly little man, padded across the hall and drew aside the draperies over an arched window to let in the sun. Another day, he thought, like all days. They went by in dismal succession, like voiceless dead men plodding to their pits, and he was one of them, without meaning or value or purpose.

Despised by his own people, a mere tool to the Romans, he had built his tower of life in gold, and dwelt in it alone.

He owned much, and had nothing. His house in Jericho was full of splendid things, but it was empty. His garden bloomed with lilac, and his extensive groves outside the city flourished with almonds, citrons and figs, but they were barren to him. His rooms were sweet with the perfume of jasmine, but it came stale to his nostrils. No neighbors came to call; no companions joined him of evenings. His wife had turned hard and biting, and he had let her go. His kinsmen avoided him except when asking for money. The hired Egyptian dancing girls became glum and resentful in his house. The servants whispered around him, and their eyes fell on him darkly.

Zaccheus climbed the stairs to the terrace chambers where he kept his accounts and began going over them with listless but mechanical efficiency.

He was a chief publican, a contractor with the Roman government to collect duties on imports and exports at towns on the main caravan routes of the province. The people hated the system, the rude searching of their belongings, the interrogations, the irregular fee-gouging, the fat profits to the private contractors. Although most chief publicans were Roman citizens, Zaccheus was a native Jew, which only intensified the contempt toward him and his subservience to the conqueror.

Slowly, doggedly, he worked through the reports. One by one, in compulsive concentration, he checked over the documents from the various way stations which he farmed out at fixed sums to subcontractors: the wheat and wine from the north . . . the camel trains from the east with Arabian tapestries, shawls and jars of precious unguents . . . the Sidonian linens . . . the complaints from owners . . . the demands for restitution . . . the rare metals, gems, multicolored cloth and grain from Egypt . . . the fish dispatched from Capernaum.

He paused, his mind still turning like a wheel, but slipping sideways as if a pinion had come loose. It had been peculiar what happened to that collector in Capernaum, a man named Matthew. He had quit his lucrative toll station to join a prophet called the Nazarene. Not many denarii in that, Zaccheus wagered. Perhaps this Matthew went mad, as indeed he felt he was doing in this grinding thralldom.

They said that Matthew had given the Nazarene a feast at the time, and the prophet had eaten with several publicans in the Herod Antipas region. For just an instant, Zaccheus' heart leaped. Perhaps I, too, he thought, could give such a feast and the Nazarene would come. But no, it was because Matthew had pledged his service. Besides, the whole tale might be false.

Zaccheus put his head down on his arms on the writing table, hiding his eyes from the light, snuffling softly in the folds of his robe. Nay, no respected man, no prophet would enter these hard precincts, this poisoned silence. I am the envied and the detested, he said to himself, the shrewd man of wealth, rejected because of what they call my ill-gotten gains. And this Nazarene must be like the rest. He does not see that I, too, crave a part of life, a grain of affection. In the marketplaces I have heard the laborers telling how the Nazarene, like the Pharisees, derides the selfish rich.

One tale was of a rich, young ruler who went running to him, kneeling, wanting to serve him, saying he had observed all the great commandments and asking what he must do to "inherit eternal life." The Nazarene had said, "One thing thou lackest: go thy way, sell whatsoever thou hast, and give to the poor, and thou shalt have treasure in heaven: and come, take up the cross, and follow me." The young man had gone away grieved, his shackles too binding to break, and the Nazarene had told his disciples, ". . . how hard is it for them that trust in riches to enter into the kingdom of God!"

The tellers of the tale said the Nazarene had smiled resignedly then and said, "It is easier for a camel to go through the eye of a needle, than for a rich man to enter into the kingdom of God." His disciples, astonished, had asked how any rich man could be saved, and he had said, ". . . with God all things are possible."

Zaccheus raised his head, blinking gloomily. Possible? What did he mean? Was each case a special one? Did each man have his own abyss, and the ways out varied? But surely the Nazarene would have nothing to do with me, both rich and a publican, no more than priests and Pharisees! Besides, they would silence even the Nazarene. I overheard only yesterday that he is returning to Judea, and the Jerusalem authorities have determined to kill him. He is a shorn lamb. They will put him on the rack and shred him to the bare bones, no matter how firm his friends. Friends! What are they? He has not seen the harshness of this world, as I have. He is not practical, as I am practical. I am tough and I have seen my chances and I have used them. Why care if they shun me and spit on my footsteps and curse my passing? I have beaten them. I have outraced them, laden my cellar with fine wines, swathed my body in silk, and built my fortune while they wasted. They covet mine! That is it! I am among the giants of the earth!

Zaccheus sat rigid, his eyes hard and opaque, his fists clenched. Then another saying of the Nazarene came to him: "Lay not up for yourselves treasures upon earth, where moth and rust doth corrupt, and where thieves break through and steal: but lay up for yourselves treasures in heaven . . . for where your treasure is, there will your heart be also. . . ."

The heart? Yea, and they will cut the heart from your breast! Thieves? A stricken look whipped across Zaccheus' face and he nearly fell from the stool getting to his feet and rushing across the stone floor to the corner, where he knelt. He glanced furtively about him, then lifted the stone and drew out the chest. He opened it and ran his hands through the heap of silver pieces and gold aurei, the jeweled figures, pearls and necklaces. He fondled the treasures for a time, squatting on the floor beside the box. Then he carefully closed it and hid it under the stone.

Something tapped him on the shoulder, not a physical touch, but a bodiless one, and he felt it just the same, felt it worming through his soft flesh, entangling him like a gray spider's web—the silence! The emptiness! He wanted to run. But he had no place to run. It was everywhere.

Back at the writing table, he tried to drown out the sensation in concentration on his business. The scratching of the pen, forming the Greek symbols required in official papers, grated loudly in the room. He worked furiously, pretending to savor the increased profits shown above the amount he must pay Rome, adjusting the count of items to preserve his gains.

When he had finished, he got up and hastened down the stairs, through the sumptuous, silent rooms and out into the garden, where the fountain swished ghostily among the shade trees and flower beds.

In recent weeks Zaccheus had taken to exercising violently in his garden, thinking it might remove some of the sluggishness from his body and the rawness from his mind. He picked up the discus, grunting, and began flinging it back and forth in the short lane. He would strain enormously, but it would go only a few feet. Then he would waddle after it, lift it with both hands and swing again feebly.

Within a few moments he limped back into the house and flopped down on a couch, panting. For a little while he lay there peacefully, his loneliness submerged in fatigue.

But it did not last long. It never lasted long. He reached behind him to a stand for a pear and munched it, listening to himself chew.

Lying there, he began to feel that he could not get up if he tried, that his body was pinned there, pressed down by forces he could not name. The feeling became stronger and stronger, and he jerked himself erect. Slowly then, he got to his feet, wretched, desolate, hungering for what he did not know, a comforting voice, a kindly look, a shared smile, a tiny measure of love.

He wandered through the silent, luxurious house, growing more tense by the moment. In his music room, where he sometimes hired choruses to play loudly throughout an evening, he sat down among the drums and cymbals and began beating them tumultuously, the noise deafening his ears and numbing his senses.

Tiring again, he stopped and sat there torpidly.

But the sound did not stop altogether. At first he thought it a derangement of his mind or hearing. But it kept coming, insistently, increasingly. It was not the crashing of cymbals, but the shouting and singing of many voices. It came from the road outside.

Zaccheus got up and hurried toward the sound. Outside, along the tree-lined road, a stream of people flowed toward the outer city limits, cheering, shouting, their faces eager and glad. Zaccheus stood in the vestibule of his house, between the two great Corinthian pillars, watching them forlornly. How, in their pennilessness, could they find such mutual delights and shared enthusiasms? He moved down the steps closer to the moving crowd, unnoticed by them, and caught snatches of their words, "It is he, Jesus . . . come again to Judaea . . . the Rabbi of Nazareth . . . the prophet they would stone."

Zaccheus felt an urge to join them, to rush into the road and throw his arms about first one and then another, to shout with them in joy, to be one with them and know what they must know and feel. His hand clutched the yoke of his robe, and he stood alone and dejected in the background, a castaway on his golden island.

Would it help a little if he raised the price of that wheat-duty post in Gophna? Or perhaps he should put an extra check point at Phasaelis to catch the trickle coming through there from Samaria. Would it help? Weren't diligence and management and attention to profits the key to success in this world?

The crowd had lined up on either side of the road, many deep, bubbling with talk, waving and stretching their necks. Far up the road, an eddy of sound rose and moved nearer. What is it? What secret does he bear them? What consummation do they find in him? I wish. . . . I would like but just a taste of it.

Zaccheus edged over toward the massed rows of people. He rose on his tiptoes, but could see only their backs. Noting a slight opening, he timidly started to move through it, brushing between the bodies. "Zaccheus!" A snarl formed his name. "Renegade . . . ! Robber!" A rough hand caught him and pulled him backward. "Drive him away . . . ! Thieving traitor!" Two hulking men shoved him from their midst. Zaccheus sprawled in the dirt.

The little man got up slowly and started to climb the steps back to his house. Then, his lips quivering, he noticed the row of palm trees running along the roadside several cubits behind the people. He moved quietly down the road a way, and tried to climb one of them. He got up a few feet and fell back down. He tried again, but with no lower branches to grasp, he fell again. He got up, puffing, his robe torn, his arms scratched and smeared with dust. His eyes cast about desperately.

Down the road he spied it—the sycamore tree. It would be easier to climb. Zaccheus ran toward it, his short legs pumping. He caught hold of a lower limb and scrambled up, kicking and pulling, and climbed until he reached the higher branches.

At once he could see the little group approaching, the Nazarene and his men. Zaccheus felt a surge of exultation. There he is! I see him! That is the one! They tried to prevent me, but I see him! Unreasoning tears came to his eyes.

The Nazarene's group came on, some of them in sackcloth, but spirit and dignity in their stride. Zaccheus had no doubt which was the Nazarene, although he had never seen him before. He was no taller than some of the others, nor broader, nor dressed differently from some, but with the strength of his step there also was a fateful gravity, a solemn awareness. Occasionally his eyes would turn toward the welcomers, smiling and compassionate.

Zaccheus watched him, transfixed, his emotions in ferment. Treasures of the heart? How? What were they? The Nazarene came nearer and nearer, and as he came, the praises swelled on either side. He walked steadily, his head slightly bowed part of the time. He came on until he reached the very spot nearest the sycamore tree, and there he stopped and looked up.

Zaccheus, panic-stricken, ducked among the leaves, struggling to conceal himself, his feet and hands slipping, his robe snagging on a branch.

"Zaccheus," Jesus called out, "make haste, and come down; for to day I must abide at thy house."

Zaccheus lost his equilibrium altogether, and a many-throated gasp came from the crowd. It seemed to Zaccheus as if he had turned upside down, and perhaps he had. Crawling, skidding, half-tumbling, his heart racing wildly, he wriggled downward, leaves flying, branches snapping, and emerged somehow upright on the ground below, dirty, winded, his hair and beard awry.

His tortured little face broke into a great, bewildered smile of gratitude, and he struggled to regain his composure, dabbing at his eyes and beckoning to the Nazarene and his men to follow him, backing up before them, nodding and gesturing and smiling appealingly at them, hoping it was real, that the Nazarene wouldn't suddenly turn and walk away, scarcely hearing the hisses and grumbles that came from the stunned crowd by the road.

He led them up the steps and, bustling like a woman, took their shoes. He clapped his hands and, the servants come running, directed them with a verve and comradely authority he had never felt before, bending to arrange the basins for his guests' feet himself, passing out towels. He poured water for the Nazarene's hands and face, repeating over and over how glad he was to have such a guest, expressing concern over the tiresome journey.

Then he led them into the dressing chambers and trotted into his own room to get his special oils for anointing their hair. As he brought combs and brushes and fresh garments, he chattered animatedly at the servants, who seemed to respond with a strange new willingness and devotion, even talking freely and asking what more was wanted. Zaccheus could not understand what had happened, except that it *had* happened, and friends were under his roof, and he loved them, and life suddenly welled in him like a warm flood, so bountiful he could hardly contain it.

Why? What is it? What brings this pulsing vitality? Is it because I and what I have are needed, are being used by my friends, by beloved strangers I never saw before, by some of humankind? "Man shall not live by bread alone . . ." the Nazarene has said. But all must have bread, and I am providing bread. Ah, but the house is beautifully astir. Perhaps it is in the providing, and not the bread at all.

That evening, after they had gathered at the table to the best that Zaccheus' stores could offer, he stood up before them, and surging with feelings he had almost forgotten, not proposing any deal or asking any return, but only doing what he knew somehow he must do, he said:

"Behold, Lord, the half of my goods I give to the poor; and if I have taken any thing from any man by false accusation, I restore him fourfold."

The Nazarene looked at him pleased, smiling confidently, sure of him. "This day," he said, "is salvation come to this house . . ."

Zaccheus bit his lip, his eyes blurring again, not comprehending just how it could be, or why, yet hearing the Nazarene speak it and believing it.

". . . the Son of man," Jesus explained, "is come to seek and to save that which was lost."

And then he told a story of a nobleman who entrusted a sum of talents (about $8,000) to three servants during his absence. On his return, two of them had used the resources and doubled them. "Well done . . ." said the nobleman, "thou hast been faithful over a few things, I will make thee ruler over many things: enter thou into the joy of thy lord."

But the third servant, infatuated with the money itself and afraid to put it to work, had kept it hidden under a stone with no gain. "Thou wicked and slothful servant . . ." said the nobleman. "Take therefore the talent from him . . . And cast ye the unprofitable servant into outer darkness . . ."

Zaccheus understood then. Fruitfulness and increase were the good things. Not the wealth itself. If valued on its own account, preserved under a stone, it both dominated and wasted, atrophied like an unused arm. It was no end, only a means. It must be ventured, used vigorously. That was it! The use made of it, the cause served. His Lord had said it:

"No man can serve two masters: for either he will hate the one, and love the other; or else he will hold to the one, and despise the other. Ye cannot serve God and mammon."

The chains of mammon had fallen from Zaccheus. He had broken free. Wealth had estranged him from his higher inheritance, had driven him into outer darkness. But he knew now it was not the wealth that mattered, but the yield. The goodly use was what partakes of life, of fellow beings, of living purposes—God's purposes.

The unexpected visitor that night had filled the void in the house of Zaccheus. The little man, tradition says, thereafter sold his great fields and freed his servants, inscribing their names and the date on potsherd under the law of manumission for slaves, giving them money and raiment. And Zaccheus himself later became Christ's bishop in Caesarea, dispensing immortal treasures on roads where once he had gathered another kind.

14

JOHN

"And Jesus entered into Jerusalem . . ."

THE TIME HAD COME. All was ready. They would soon see what lay in store. Swiftly John folded his cloak on the little gray burro's back, smoothed it out evenly, and stepped aside. The Master mounted and sat sideways. A quick, comradely smile passed between the two men. They started off.

The high walls and turrets of Jerusalem gleamed in the sun. Strains of pure, sweet melody drifted across the valley from the Temple, standing high above the city. The sun turned its whiteness to a million dancing jewels. It was spring, a few days before Passover, and fresh greenery laced the olive and cypress trees hugging the road. A zestful tang was in the air. The youthful John snapped a twig off an overhanging limb and flicked it spinning through the air.

The little group rounded the side of the tree-swathed

Mount of Olives, leaving behind them the village of Bethany, and started down the cut-stone Jericho road that dipped across the valley of Kidron and rose on the other side to the city gates. John strode briskly along beside the burro, anxiety mingling with his eagerness.

Ahead was a crucial test. John could sense it, see it in the guarded, uncertain glances of the others, hear it in their taut, muted conversation, read it in the Master's deep preoccupation. There was indeed ample cause for worry. Just a few days ago, the Master had spoken disturbingly about the chief priests delivering him up to the Roman rulers, who would "scourge him and . . . kill him"—but in three days he would rise again!

John's steps slowed momentarily. Appalling words, and strange. Yet the Master might have been speaking in parables as he so often had before. Besides, Jesus could not be overcome or defeated. Never! And by all the evidence, with the great feast approaching, the pilgrims gathering and the special mood of the Master, a great turning point must be at hand. Was Jesus about to begin a new phase in the building of his kingdom? John had yearned for him to assert his supremacy more strongly, and whatever the method, he had unbounded trust that it would excel and endure. How did that old prophecy go? ". . . behold, thy King cometh . . . lowly, and riding upon an ass . . ." Not before had Jesus gone to a place riding. John could not restrain a surge of confidence.

Fiery and intense, John had awaited the moment for nearly three years, giving up his well-to-do home and servants, leaving his place in his father's big fishing business, even overriding his father's objections in order to go with the Master. At times, Jesus had had to temper the younger man's ardent enthusiasms. Just the other day, for example, John had proposed violent punishment for a Samaritan village that had refused hospitality to the Master. "Lord," John had said, his eyes snapping, "wilt thou that we command fire to come down from heaven, and consume them . . . ?" Jesus had promptly corrected him. ". . . the Son of man is not come to destroy men's lives, but to save them." Then, near Bethsaida, John had seen some hairy-mantled teacher acting in Jesus' name, yet refusing to accompany their band. John, in his zeal for the cause, had wanted to prohibit the man from continuing the work alone. But the Master would impose no narrow, exclusive conformity. "Forbid him not," he had said, "for he that is not against us is for us."

Despite John's flaring disposition, Jesus held him in particular affection, tolerating his impatient drive, knowing his fervid loyalty, his immense dedication—calling him Ben-reges—"Son of Thunder." On several intimate occasions, as when Jesus was transfigured on the high mountain, only John, James, his older, more disciplined brother, and the leader, Peter, had been present.

Now, at the point of what seemed a critical decision, keen urgency drove John as they approached Jerusalem, seat of all Israel. The land was astir with talk of a coming Christ—a new kingdom to throw off Rome's yoke. Down in the valley sprawled the tents of the pilgrims, thousands of them come here for the great festival, spreading out from the little camps of Silwan and of Gihon with their crowded hovels of the poor, just outside the city wall.

John's legs stretched out in long, reaching strides, his arms swinging widely at his sides. At intervals he had to pause to keep from leaving the rest behind. Somehow, in spite of all the somber intimations of the Master, an irresistible exuberance filled him on this bracing, important morning. He had been waiting for it, getting set for it, all during these last two months that they had spent in and about the isolated little town of Ephraim.

On the way here, when Jesus had spoken ominously of what lay ahead, John's spirits had been undampened.

Jesus had asked, ". . . can ye drink of the cup that I drink of?"

Both John and his brother affirmed stoutly, "We can." This peppery pair was ready for the general conflict, to stand shoulder to shoulder with the Master in his magnificence, but they didn't foresee what the specific requirements might be.

They were so eager that they had begun maneuvering for a choice position in the Master's reign. "Grant unto us," they had said, "that we may sit, one on thy right hand, and the other on thy left hand, in thy glory."

It wasn't that simple, Jesus had told them. He said they would, indeed, eventually share the ordeal of raising his emblem. But it wouldn't be the kind of prominence suggested by their ambitions.

". . . whosoever will be chief among you, let him be your servant," he had said. "Even as the Son of man came not to be ministered unto, but . . . to give his life a ransom for many."

Now John glanced over at the Master, swaying gently on the burro. The animal's tiny hooves stepped mincingly along the smooth, close-set stones. Jesus' eyes burned with a remote fire, a distant musing.

As they neared the foot of the slope, John's ears at first mistook the sound that came to him as the usual clamor of life in the valley settlements, but then he looked up the road and saw what it really was. He uttered a cry of delight. Pleasure shone suddenly on the faces of the others, too. James broke into a smile. Big, commanding Peter threw out his chest, and even gloomy Thomas wore a surprised twinkle.

Ahead of them, filling the road and still streaming out of the city gate, moving toward them across the bridge, came a multitude of people, waving palm branches and shouting praises of the Master. Even before the crowd reached them, John caught some of their words. "Hosanna! Blessed be the King that cometh in the name of the Lord . . ." Surely, he thought, a time of triumph is here.

The disciples, their worries suddenly vanished, caught up in unexpected joy, burst out singing. They sang loudly, stepping in time to their singing. John heard Thomas' voice soaring above the rest, and he himself joined in spiritedly.

The welcoming throng divided to both sides of the road as it met Jesus, spreading cloaks on the stones ahead of him, strewing the road with flowers and green leaves. "Hosanna!" They shouted it over and over again. "Blessed be the kingdom of our father David, that cometh in the name of the Lord: Hosanna in the highest." Men, women and children filled the air with praise. "Peace in heaven, and glory in the highest."

They waved palm branches, and fathers held their little ones on their shoulders so that they, too, could see the Master. All across the valley, standing on the banks of the brook beside the bridge, they crowded the road into the city.

Tears spilled down Jesus' cheeks.

It was an hour of greatness, John thought. At his keen pitch of exhilaration, he considered it only a passing triviality when some of the religious authorities shoved through the crowd and shouted for Jesus to stop the demonstration—at once. John relished Jesus' blunt retort —that if the followers of the Lord were silenced, the very stones of the earth would cry out in protest.

All along the way, up past the cemetery of white burial urns and vaults, and on through the northeast city gate, the welcomers laid a verdant carpet for the Master and hailed his name. Townspeople clambered to their flat roofs and outside stairways to see what went on, swarming like ants over the white buildings.

The course into the city left a wake of speculation and wonder. Who is this? was the question John heard all around. And the reply from the greeters: This is Jesus the prophet of Nazareth of Galilee.

Most of the crowd dispersed after Jesus had dismounted and entered briefly into the Temple. Only then did John begin to realize that, though the throng had included great numbers of devoted followers, many had been attracted to it solely out of curiosity. Still, it was keenly heartening, and John hungered for further gains. The Master, however, remained intensely solemn. In the midst of a conversation, shortly after the cheering welcome, he became deeply introspective and depressed, speaking almost as if to himself. "Now is my soul troubled—" he paused—"and what shall I say? Father, save me from this hour: but for this cause came I unto this hour." He fell silent, then added forcefully, "Father, glorify thy name."

Whatever all this implied, John thought, the Master clearly was on the verge of some momentous step.

Jesus returned to Bethany for the night, but came back daily to the city. Official opposition closed in grimly. But it only seemed to stir the Master to new boldness. Never had John heard him speak so vehemently. He had always been positive but patient; now he seemed to be deliberately pressing toward a result, a culmination. John waited, watched and listened, his emotions aflame.

As the days before the Passover went by, priests, their lawyers and other functionaries came to challenge Jesus at gatherings in the Temple courts with sly innuendo and devious questions. Repeatedly, Jesus explained his identity with God, but he grew short with the insincere baiters.

"By what authority doest thou these things?" they demanded.

Jesus shot back a counterquestion, asking them if John the Baptist had had God's authority or not. They couldn't say yes, because they didn't accept the Baptist, but if they said no, the people wouldn't stand for it. They hemmed and hawed and at length replied, "We cannot tell."

"Neither tell I you by what authority I do these things."

John grinned.

They belabored him about taxes, the law and his teachings, trying to trap him, but he confounded them with his answers: Pay Caesar what is Caesar's. The great commandments are alike—love God and thy neighbor as thyself. Self-glory is ruinous. To help the sick, naked and imprisoned is to serve the Lord.

All the while, there was the gathering hostility of men in high places. John could sense it in the numbers of soldiers, Sadducean priests, their guards and clean-shaven Herodian party members that trailed Jesus about, watching him, like animals lying in wait. But the Master lashed out heedlessly at the reigning theocracy, accusing it of being obsessed with ornamental clothes, riches, titles, honors; of pretending holiness by reciting long, repetitious prayers; of emphasizing moribund rules and forms instead of real mercy, faith and justice.

"Woe unto you, scribes and Pharisees, hypocrites!" he said. ". . . Ye blind guides, which strain at a gnat, and swallow a camel . . . ye are like unto whited sepulchres, which indeed appear beautiful outward, but are within full of dead men's bones . . ."

The tension mounted. Jesus strode into the outer courts of the Temple, denouncing the noisy, profitable commerce carried on there by the Sadducean priesthood—the money-changing, the selling of doves and livestock for sacrifice. "Take these things hence. . ." he ordered, and began overturning tables and driving out the pack of them, traders and beasts. "It is written," he said, "My house shall be called the house of prayer; but ye have made it a den of thieves." John had not expected such turbulence, even though he had favored just that before. He saw the brawny Temple guards start forward, then hang back, irresolute before the crowd supporting Jesus. The Master grabbed a whip from one of the guards and hied the animals out, lambs kicking up their heels, and pigeons taking flight. For the moment he virtually controlled the Temple precincts.

John, the firebrand, wondered at it all. He had wanted strong action. And yet . . . Brought face to face with the world's entrenched enmity, he hesitated. Like the others, he paled in the sharp glare of open encounter. It was part of spiritual growing up, of casting off the heady dreams of quick glory, of recognizing that they traveled a course not of sudden acclaim or royal coronations, but of sacrifice. John's uneasiness grew at the hauntingly memorable meal in the upper room where Jesus spoke of imminent betrayal and death, and then when the armed mob seized him in Gethsemane, John and the other apostles slunk away in frightened confusion. Only John, however, the impassioned apostle who proposed force, yet who shrank at its consequences, returned to stand by Jesus at his trial and execution. He may have once been overeager for that throne on high, in too big a hurry. But Jesus, in this time of ultimates, righted the erring perspectives, vitalized his words and sharpened the vision. The kingdom would come in its own time, by the inexorable unfolding of the Lord. John could work and wait, and he did, helping erect for the centuries a sovereignty maintained not by honored thrones, but by dogged faith.

15

PHILIP

*"And he . . . went, as he was wont, to
the mount of Olives . . ."*

HE HAD SEEN, but he did not see. He
had heard, but he did not understand.
He had accepted, but he did not know.
Philip believed, but he wanted tangible
proof.

"Lord," he asked Jesus, "shew us the Father, and it
sufficeth us."

After all this time, after the many months of mutual
labor, after the long, painstaking efforts of Jesus to explain
and clarify, to illustrate, enact and make plain, Philip still
sought something more, something bigger, a final clincher.

Jesus, there in his last hours, turned to him and spread
his rough leathery hands in a gesture of dismayed entreaty. "Have I been so long time with you, and yet hast
thou not known me, Philip?"

The question, the surprised pain on the Master's face,

hurled Philip back, back over the dusty miles, back to the camps and cities and congregations he had visited with Jesus, back to the deserts and valleys they had crossed, the people, old and young, whose lives Jesus had touched with newness, the words spoken, the work done. Wasn't it enough? Couldn't he be sure? Out of the memorable panorama of events and evidences, the array of experiences and insights, couldn't he be positive? Could it all be illusion?

Philip, who had a wife and several daughters at his home in Bethsaida on the northern tip of the lake of Galilee, was a mild, genial man, with a practical outlook, many friends, and a settled, easygoing disposition. He was well educated, with a solid grasp of Scripture and a ready appreciation of the progress of sciences. Black of hair and fair of skin, he had Greek family ties and associations, and a Greek name.

Like the Greeks, Philip inclined toward a materialistic view of life: the physical senses determined truth. Only what could be weighed, measured and observed by man was real. Valid ideas must be confirmed by substance, by reasoned deduction, by visible proofs, the calculations of astronomers or mathematicians. Facts must pass the test of the body and its faculties.

But was there something else? Something outside the usual ken of man that he could know, that he could trust and rely on, for certain?

Philip was never overbearing or forward in his attitudes. But he prided himself on his balance, his cautious judgment and common sense. He had served the Master conscientiously. But his careful mind would not be rushed into conclusions.

Standing there now on the moonlit road leading out of Jerusalem toward the Garden of Gethsemane, with Jesus' poignant question hanging over him, with the other disciples waiting for his reply, Philip's thoughts flooded with recollections. Like a restless river, they flowed through him, the moments, the places, the faces of men and women, the afflictions turned into vigor, the crutches tossed jubilantly away, the blind seeing the sun, the tears become laughter, the lost sheep brought home—the bursting splendor of faith. How had it all happened? What was behind it all? Certainly not the tricks of legerdemain, the workings of some masterful magician. No, Jesus spurned such ostentation. His connection with the needs of men ran in some deep, indefinable channel.

". . . thy faith hath made thee whole." That's what he kept telling them. To believe . . . if they would only believe. It was an impalpable thing within themselves, between themselves and Jesus, between men and the core of life. But how could one verify it?

There was that time the woman, the frail, sick woman with the hemorrhage, pushed through the crowd following Jesus and merely touched his garment. In the thick movement of the throng, Jesus obviously felt not the touch, but that mystic thing, belief.

"Who touched my clothes?" he asked, turning, and then he saw her. "Daughter, be of good comfort; thy faith hath made thee whole."

Strange, baffling, unexplainable. . . .

There was that time on the road near Jericho when the two blind men kept wailing, "... mercy ... mercy ..." They made Philip uncomfortable. Others sought to silence them. But Jesus would not pass them by. The force of conviction—the certainty of recovery—throbbed in their cries.

"Believe ye," Jesus asked them, "that I am able to do this?"

"Yea, Lord," they affirmed.

And Jesus said, "According to your faith be it unto you."

The men shouted with happiness—for they could see.

Because of faith? How did that matter? Why not because of deeds? Why not because of the Master's power? Why didn't he simply take credit for the marvel?

But he clearly wanted no sensationalism, no reputation as a miracle doer which would only excite the curious. "See that no man know it," he kept telling the healed, the cleansed and rejuvenated. But they spread it widely, nonetheless.

He seemed determined to rivet attention on his teachings instead, on his enduring counsel—rather than the unusual incidents. He acted as if everything hinged on some important, inner condition, the harmonies of the heart, and not the outer appearances. "It is the spirit that quickeneth," he said. "The flesh profiteth nothing: the words that I speak unto you, they are spirit, and they are life. . . ."

There was that time on the mountain with the five thousand men, besides women and children, many of them far from their home villages and without food. Jesus had asked Philip, "Whence shall we buy bread, that these may eat?" It had not been a normal question, but more like a test, as if the Master were asking Philip to prove himself.

Philip, devoid of any idea except the conventional solution, had made a flustered, rough calculation and said, "Two hundred pennyworth [$40] of bread is not sufficient for them, that every one of them may take a little."

All they had had were five loaves and two small fishes which a lad had brought to Andrew. But Jesus had bade the multitude sit down on the green grass, by orderly companies of hundreds and fifties. Then he had turned his eyes heavenward, giving thanks. "Blessed art thou, O Lord our God . . . who has brought forth bread upon the earth."

Philip had had no inkling what Jesus would then do. But he had blessed the tiny portion, broken it and passed it to the disciples to distribute. They had moved, uncertainly at first, among the seated people, giving each some, and remarkably the little bread became abundance in their mouths, and all were filled and content, and nourishment aplenty remained at the banquet spread by Jesus.

But Philip and other disciples misconstrued the whole episode, thinking it pertained strictly to food. Jesus appealed to them later, ". . . perceive ye not yet, neither understand? have ye your heart yet hardened?" The feeding had not been intended just for ordinary appetites, but as a symbol of his teaching, which endowed with abundance the spirit of man. "How is it," Jesus beseeched them, "that ye do not understand that I spake it not to you concerning bread . . . ?" Again, he was pointing to that unseen, unseeable element, whatever it was, that inner need, or hunger, that is not satisfied by wonders or baskets of bread. "Having eyes, see ye not?" Jesus had continued, "and having ears, hear ye not? . . . How is it that ye do not understand?"

It would, perhaps, have been clearer to Philip if Jesus simply had provided supernatural displays, done amazing feats, called lightning from a cloudless sky, made a hillside crumble, or a man fly as a bird. This was the kind of thing most men recognized and understood, that impressed them. But did such things have lasting weight?

". . . we would see a sign from thee," the skeptics kept saying.

"There shall no sign be given . . ."

Philip, too, with all his devotion, had yielded to that desire for a sign, a flagrant demonstration. Yet it was not in criticism, but only because his practical, earthly mind searched for an easier way, a more obvious, limited concept. But Jesus would have none of it. "If I honour myself, my honour is nothing . . ." He had kept the stress on his relationship to ordinary mortals, on that intangible, spiritual adherence to him which he called the secret of wholeness.

There was that time at the house of Jairus, the distraught Pharisee whose daughter lay as if lifeless. ". . . the maid is not dead," Jesus said, "but sleepeth." The people laughed at him. Intelligent people laughed him to scorn. But not Jairus. He did not laugh. He wanted his daughter, wanted her alive, wanted it so badly he could not give up. And Jesus, saying that Jairus truly believed, took the girl by the hand, and she sat up.

Did it prove anything? Perhaps the girl only had been sleeping, although that was a common Jewish euphemism for death. Was Jesus implying that life itself resided in belief . . . in faith? Philip remembered how many times he and others among the twelve had appealed to Jesus, "Increase our faith."

It was hard to know. It was hard to be convinced unalterably, to be sure always. Philip, like the others, had been deeply moved when Jesus commissioned them to heal the sick and troubled. And, imitating him, they had done much good. But sometimes they could do nothing.

Philip would not forget the epileptic boy who went into fits of wallowing, foaming, tearing himself, throwing himself into water or fire, with ensuing periods of pining listlessness. The disciples could not help him, and they asked Jesus why. "Because of your unbelief . . ." He was disappointed with them. "O faithless generation, how long shall I be with you? how long shall I suffer you?" The question still lingered in Philip . . . How long?

Jesus had told the boy's father, "If thou canst believe, all things are possible to him that believeth." That resounding word. Belief! All things from believing! Again, Jesus had shifted the attention from himself to that mysterious response within the boy's father, who shut his eyes, moaning, "Lord, I believe; help thou mine unbelief."

A confusing mixture! Were the phrases not contradictory? But no, somehow in the earnest effort of belief, there existed belief itself, for Jesus had spoken to the child, who then became well.

Philip remembered, too, that time in the flash storm

on the Galilee lake, when waves towered high and crashed on the boat. Jesus was sleeping. Philip had hung to a cross brace in terror. Others were flung about, wild-eyed, their shouts swallowed in the uproar. They awakened Jesus. "Lord, save us . . . carest thou not that we perish?"

Jesus arose, rebuking them. "Where is your faith?" In the sudden tumult, he still spoke of faith. "Peace, be still." In the roaring storm, like those that come so often, his voice and presence were like a mighty anchor, a safe harbor. "Why are ye so fearful? how is it ye have no faith?" The wind was no longer fierce or threatening. There was no longer any danger. There was respite and security.

Philip remembered his awe, and that of the others. Had Jesus actually stilled the wind? Or had it quieted suddenly by coincidence? Or had his influence quelled their panic and made the sea seem harmless? Whatever the fact, he had, once again, summoned up faith—and delivered them from chaos. It had left Philip thoroughly bemused.

Then there was the Roman centurion who came asking help for his servant, grievously tormented with palsy. The officer said that because of his military status, his house was unworthy for Jesus to enter, but that if Jesus would only speak the word, the servant would be healed. 'Verily," Jesus said, ". . . I have not found so great faith . . . Go thy way; and as thou hast believed, so be it done unto thee." And the servant was cured.

There was the Phoenician woman on the coast of Tyre, pleading for aid for her sick daughter. "O woman," Jesus said, "great is thy faith: be it unto thee even as thou wilt." There was blind Bartimaeus, craving his sight. "Go thy way; thy faith hath made thee whole." There were the lepers, the lame, the mad, the starving, the watery-eyed, half-naked beggars, and there was the compassion of Jesus, who kindled in these cast-off lives a great thing—faith.

The moments, the feelings, the strange but simple goodness of it poured through Philip, both troubling and exciting him.

It had been more than two years since Jesus had come and found Philip, and enlisted his service. Jesus had had to seek him out, because with Philip's pragmatic, unimaginative nature, he himself had not been actively looking for any wider vision. But Jesus had wanted him, apparently seeing him as a crucible, a testing ground for the lessons of the spirit, a necessary ally to be gained in a pragmatic world.

So, after all the seasons of traveling and teaching, they had come here to Jerusalem for the Passover, shared a supper in an upper room in the city, and as they walked out toward the city gates, Jesus had begun speaking to them, ". . . I go to prepare a place for you. . . . I am the way, the truth, and the life: no man cometh unto the Father, but by me. . . . from henceforth ye know him, and have seen him."

It was at this point that Philip broke in, declaring on an impulse that he still wanted ultimate proof. ". . . shew us the Father . . ." That would erase all question marks, Philip thought at the moment. It would overcome all hesitations and resistance. No matter how dubious a man might be, this would provide conspicuous, irrefutable evidence.

Jesus had halted, and they stood there in the road now, his staggered disappointment suspended in the night air. ". . . hast thou not known me, Philip?"

As the memories engulfed him, Philip bowed his head, unable to speak. It seemed an endless moment, and as the memories pounded through him, he realized he had asked a foolish thing, that he still did not know all the answers, but that they would not be found in dazzling spectacles—but rather in the steadfast temples of the heart.

". . . he that hath seen me," Jesus said quietly, "hath seen the Father; and how sayest thou then, Shew us the Father?"

Shame gripped Philip, and he put his hands over his eyes, all the gentle, patient but strong ways of Jesus converging on him. No, no, he did not want any glaring signs or exhibitions. Not now. Not after he had really considered what he had said.

Such things might stir up a few people, at any given moment, but in the years that followed, others would only sneer at such accounts, call them fables, and demand more grandiose displays, more proofs, more evidence that they could touch and see and hear. That was the realm they lived in; the realm, perhaps, he had once lived in. Philip shook his head, his hands hiding his eyes.

People were always wanting signs. They wanted a show. They wanted concrete objects. They wanted digits and numbers and equations put down in black and white.

That was all that their inverted minds knew, all that their myopic eyes saw.

They did not believe beyond themselves. They huddled within their narrow walls. They barred the gates and rejected all else. Oh, yes, they liked to sing of the stars, but that was only because the stars were baldly visible. They did not perceive the grander heights of the soul. And this was what Jesus had been trying to tell them.

Philip dropped his arms and looked at the Master, a look of complete, unquestioning faith.

"Believest thou not," Jesus asked, "that I am in the Father, and the Father in me?"

Philip nodded slowly, fervently, his throat constricted. Jesus' gaze was like a strong, silent handclasp.

They walked on then, the disciples and Jesus, out of the city toward the Kidron valley and the garden on the Mount of Olives. Jesus continued to speak as they walked.

". . . the words that I speak unto you I speak not of myself: but the Father that dwelleth in me . . . And I will pray the Father, and he shall give you another Comforter, that he may abide with you forever; even the Spirit of truth . . . I will not leave you comfortless . . . Yet a little while, and the world seeth me no more; but ye see me: because I live, ye shall live also. . . ."

As they passed through the still night, Philip felt a new stamina in his step, a firmer beat in his veins. It had been difficult for him, in his earthbound notions, to comprehend the infinite workings of Jesus in man. But in that moment there on the dark road, when Philip's eyes could see little, he had seen much, and he knew and he believed. And therein lay the mainspring and the miracle.

"... If ye have faith, and doubt not ... if ye shall say unto this mountain, Be thou removed, and ... cast into the sea; it shall be done," Jesus had said. "And all things, whatsoever ye shall ask in prayer, believing, ye shall receive."

Jesus had come to man, not with extravagant performances and shocking magic, but with an even truer wonder, a more lasting and prodigious disclosure—God's bond to men, and the power of faith in him, of belief. Perhaps no man could achieve it entirely. But he could move toward it, seeing its ultimate in Jesus. Philip, even though prone to the world's vacillating kind of knowledge, had discovered the fuller, unchanging wisdom, and after Jesus left him and the others to carry on the work, Philip did so with fervor, declaring that there was above all one invisible, immeasurable, indefinable essential for baptism in Christ:

"If thou believest with all thine heart ..."

16

CAIAPHAS

". . . and the chief priests and the scribes sought how they might . . . put him to death."

WITH BOTH FINALITY and finesse, Joseph Caiaphas had laid his plans, but he had found no opportunity to carry them out, and the delay chafed him like nettles against the flesh. He had to strike soon, or face even more vexing obstacles. The stern eyes of Rome allowed for no dawdling.

It was two days before the Passover. Caiaphas, the small, delicate-bodied high priest of Jerusalem, hurried through his morning bath, directing his attendants in sharp, waspish monosyllables.

For four days now, this incendiary Galilean had been roaming the city, whipping up an ever larger following, and there had been no appropriate chance to seize him without starting a furor. At least, the bungling guards had failed to find one. As Caiaphas saw it, his exalted office, his prestige, his power, the entire hegemony of the priest-hood were in jeopardy. These could be lost to Rome if he didn't deal conclusively with the disturber. And all he had been able to do was wait . . . wait . . . wait! Even his own family smarted over it—mainly his wife's father, Annas. He knew what to do, he knew how to do it; but he had to find the right situation.

Some leaders of the Sanhedrin would arrive later in the morning to discuss the rankling business. Caiaphas had little information to give them. And that was the crux of his predicament—lack of information. Where did this brazen Galilean go when he left his daytime assemblies? When could he be arrested quietly in private? The man had gained such popularity that any public arrest might start a riot. Such disorder would force Roman troops into action; and since military displays always fanned Jewish resentment, an irritated Rome would have grounds for charging the priesthood with incompetency, possibly for further reducing its authority. That would not do. Caiaphas, a shrewd artist in the subtleties of statecraft, knew better than to permit such an error to be charged to him. He wanted the matter handled neatly, coolly and un-conditionally.

His bath finished, he stood for a moment, holding his slender, blue-veined hands over the coals burning on the tripods.

Delay also sharpened dangers. With this upstart be-ing hailed as the Messiah, stimulating Jewish belief in a native king to rule the world, Rome might be impelled to assume firmer control. This, too, could cost the religious government its remaining prerogatives.

Within this delicate mesh of power lay Caiaphas' dilemma.

He stepped out from the curtains around the bathing cubicle and began getting into his vestments, the long *haluk* that reached to his knees and, over this, the tight-fitted *kuttoneth*. Levitical attendants fidgeted, tying the bands on the sleeves, and he fussed at them snappishly to get on with it.

He had to find some way to speed events.

More than two months ago he had sealed the fate of this disruptive do-gooder from Galilee, when the report of his raising a man named Lazarus from death had swept the city. Caiaphas recalled now the weak-kneed stammering at the time of some of the lawyers and Pharisees in the Sanhedrin, even some of his own fellow Sadducees who controlled the priesthood as well as the lawmaking and judicial body.

"What do we?" they asked, fluttering their hands, "for this man doeth many miracles. If we let him thus alone, all men will believe on him: and the Romans shall come and take away both our place and nation."

Caiaphas had let them babble on for a while, and then cut them off sharply. "Ye know nothing at all." Right then, peremptorily and unequivocally, he had told them what would be done. ". . . it is expedient for us, that one man should die for the people, and that the whole nation perish not."

Caiaphas half-chuckled, remembering the scene. For

all his slight build, he had the cleverness and the grit to rule the moods of weaker men.

It didn't make any difference to him how the Galilean died, or what the legal formulations. Such matters could be arranged. Nor did it make any difference what the man's spiritual endowments or ideas. Irrelevant chaff! Leave such things to those pedantic, puritanical commoners, the Pharisees. What mattered to Caiaphas was the preservation of his and the Sadducean hierarchy's control over written laws, the prescribed rituals, the taxes, tithes, local civil trade, and the huge revenues from the Temple. To hold on to these quasi-independent powers under Roman dominion required expert manipulation—a pursuit in which Caiaphas took due pride. He had ignored the Galilean as long as he was a mere thorn in the side of his counterparts, the Pharisees, but when popular support made him an issue in practical politics, Caiaphas and his party readied the noose.

The man was clearly a subversive, undermining established institutions. His heretical notions, whatever they were, were too persuasive. They had to be eliminated. The naïve populace had to be protected from such teachings. They threatened the government's security.

Why, the man even assailed the fundamental law of retaliatory justice which held that as a man does, so shall it be done unto him, "breach for breach, eye for eye, tooth for tooth . . ." Mosaic law, Roman law, the Hammurabic code all agreed on this. But this Galilean advocated some devious theory of turning the other cheek, claiming revenge is not sweet and only an endless chain of strife. Ha!

Fully garbed now, Caiaphas took a chair and submitted to the ministrations of his Assyrian hairdresser. Usually he savored the daily session. But not today.

The hairdresser spread an apron over the high priest's chest and went to work with aromatic oils and instruments, curling and anointing his beard and earlocks.

Caiaphas sat there, his thin face immobile, his canny eyes staring out fixedly. He had to bide his time. He had to wait. He had to proceed circumspectly. No more of these muddled attempts to frighten the Galilean with stones. Some of the religious commoners had tried that in the past. Caiaphas would do it his way. He would do it smoothly, within the framework of law. He knew the technique. At that session two months ago he had issued his command that if any of his approximately five thousand priests or guards knew of the Galilean's whereabouts in Jerusalem at any time, they should report it so that the arrest could be made. But until this week, the man had dropped out of sight, reportedly in hiding near the village of Ephraim. Now he had returned on a crest of public adulation that thwarted any open seizure.

An icy wave went through Caiaphas, remembering the cheering mob that had gone out to escort the Galilean into the city. Aides had come running to Caiaphas, bleating, "Perceive ye how ye prevail nothing? behold, the world is gone after him."

The inane blubberers! He didn't want their plaintive hand-wringing, but information, vigilance, facts about the man's habits. He wanted the guards to catch the man without crowds about. But the only result had been that one of his officers came fretting, "Never man spake like this man." Caiaphas could deal with that. "Are ye also deceived?"

Remembering the officer's look of fear at the aspersion cast on his own loyalty, Caiaphas sniggered, then restrained himself.

He heard the voices of his ministers gathering in the hall below, and made short with the rest of his toilet. He slipped on his broidered coat and jeweled miter, cleared his throat and descended the stairs, making sure he displayed no anxiety or ado, maintaining his unassailable dignity.

Several of the chief priests were there, some of the legal specialists, the scribes and lawyers, and a few aging elders. Naturally, Annas had come over. His palace and that of Caiaphas were connected by an enclosed corridor.

The old man, ousted as high priest about fifteen years ago for using the death penalty without the required Roman confirmation, still retained great influence. Three years after his removal, when Caiaphas married his daughter, he had helped his son-in-law become high priest. Today he was in a trembling rage about new forays by the Galilean. The interloper had caused havoc in the Temple markets, disrupting the money-changing and the sale of sacrificial animals. Annas ran both of these profitable concessions. He snorted and fulminated. The villainy! The banditry!

This latest offense inflamed emotions as the group assembled in the palace council chamber, off to one side of the great hall. Heatedly they reviewed the situation, the potentialities. Prompt, effective measures must be taken. The councilors agreed: Jesus must be taken by stealth and brought to death. Caiaphas, who had decided that much long ago, heard them out, his eyes opaque, his lips a dark slit between the neat folds of his beard. Yet the execution, they said, must not be "on the feast day, lest there be an uproar among the people."

On that note, the meeting disbanded. It left Caiaphas with today, tonight and tomorrow to accomplish his objective, else the Galilean might disappear again for months. It left him with his same dilemma.

He summoned his guard officers from the Temple and instructed them to maintain continuous surveillance of the Galilean so as to discern an occasion on which to waylay him quietly. He told them to disguise themselves in ordinary dress, to follow the man to private haunts.

And then, more waiting. . . .

Caiaphas picked at his noon meal, the food gravel in his mouth. He ordered a servant to fasten the draperies tighter on the high windows around the upper landing. The spring air had a bite to it. His fragile body could not seem to assimilate heat.

Still he waited. He could do nothing until the proper moment arrived. He had to wait. He paced the floor, feeling like a man in bonds. Annas came over and lectured him on the urgent need for action, and left grumbling. The family heritage was at stake. Caiaphas conferred with his chief guards again. He waited.

Then it happened.

In midafternoon, an officer came breathlessly to the

palace. One of the Galilean's men had volunteered to guide authorities to his leader's rendezvous that night. Caiaphas ordered the informer brought into his presence. This was what he had been waiting for.

The man was a short, surly-looking recreant, no taller than Caiaphas and almost as thin, yet more rugged and heavier boned. He shifted his feet, ill at ease in the presence of such eminence. "What will ye give me," he asked, "and I will deliver him unto you?"

Caiaphas concealed his contempt, but also his elation. With stately decorum, he assured the informer that he was performing a patriotic service, but he also impressed upon the man his own complicity—for which his duty to the nation should atone. Caiaphas knew that by frightening him a little he could buy him the more cheaply.

Give him thirty pieces of silver (about $25), Caiaphas instructed. It was counted out. The informer took it uncertainly. He was instructed in detail about bringing word of the Galilean's movements that night, and dismissed.

Again Caiaphas waited, but now with self-congratulatory relish.

As a preliminary, arrangements had been made with the Roman governor, Pilate, to supply troops to make the arrest when the time came. Soldiers would be available at call at the Fortress Antonia, adjoining the Temple. Roman officers were in on the plan. After all, placating them was a major motive.

Several hours after dark, the informer brought word of the Galilean's whereabouts, and was sent off with the chief guard officers to join the soldiers at the fortress and go after the prey.

While they were on their mission, Caiaphas kept busy getting word to trusted cohorts in the Sanhedrin to convene at his palace. It required twenty-three for a quorum of the seventy-man body. Holding a criminal trial at night was illegal. So were some of the other procedures. But haste was essential. A traitor could not be allowed sanctuary in regulations. To give a semblance of legality, however, Caiaphas sent priests and guards to ferret about the city for willing witnesses. Not that they actually mattered. Judgment already had been passed.

Presently he heard the clanking of weapons and the tramp of boots in the courtyard, and knew the victim was in the net. They took him first into the house of Annas next door, and Caiaphas stood by, letting the old man have the satisfaction of badgering the prisoner awhile. The Galilean stood there impassively, docile but unabashed, his arms bound to his sides. A philosophical-looking fellow. Not a likely type for a revolutionary, Caiaphas thought, but no doubt a lion of rhetoric. Annas ragged him with barbed questions, trying to jolt some damning evidence out of him. But the man apparently sensed the trap.

"I spake openly to the world," he said. "I ever taught in the synagogue, and in the temple . . . in secret have I said nothing. Why askest thou me? ask them which heard me, what I have said unto them . . ."

The impudence! A guard stepped up and struck a cracking blow to his face. The prisoner caught himself from falling and still stood there, impenitent. "If I have spoken evil, bear witness of the evil . . ." he said. Annas snorted in disgust.

Still bound, the captive was hustled through the corridor to Caiaphas' palace, where a bare, selected quorum of the Sanhedrin had gathered, along with a few witnesses, known sycophants who would say anything for attention.

They gave varying accounts. One said, "We heard him say, I will destroy this temple that is made with hands, and within three days I will build another made without hands." Others gave different versions. None of them agreed on what he had said.

Caiaphas, his patience at an end, arose and confronted the prisoner coldly. "Answerest thou nothing?"

There was no response.

"What is it which these witness against thee?" Caiaphas insisted, putting grisly implications in the question.

Still the renegade stood silent, unblinking.

Caiaphas' eyes were like black frost. "I adjure thee by the living God, that thou tell us whether thou be the Christ, the Son of God."

The prisoner looked at him, unimpressed. "Thou hast said." Then he sighed, giving them their way. "Nevertheless I say unto you, Hereafter shall ye see the Son of man sitting on the right hand of power, and coming in the clouds of heaven."

". . . blasphemy!" Caiaphas shouted. He ripped his own resplendent garments, the action signifying that he had heard blasphemy with his own ears. Reliable followers on the Sanhedrin joined in the demonstration. "What further need have we of witnesses?" Caiaphas urged them on. "Behold, now ye have heard his blasphemy. What think ye?" He knew he had them built up for the kill.

"He is guilty of death." They chorused it, swept along by their self-righteous wrath, their clothes torn, their faces white and twisted, beating their fists on their breasts. Any protests were lost in the outburst.

They did not, however, sentence the man to die, for they knew that they didn't have the power. That would be up to Rome. And Caiaphas, a nice tactician, would adhere to the formalities to protect his position.

He walked away, leaving the guards and the others to torment the prisoner. They had to have their satisfactions, too. He went and stood by the fire, a faint warmth coming over him. He had done well. He had out maneuvered Rome in the toils of power. He had molded men and events. But he still had to prepare for the presentation tomorrow before the procurator. That should be easy. Let Pilate squirm now.

They took the prisoner to the dungeon beneath the Temple that night, and early next morning, as a hasty formality, put him before the Sanhedrin in its regular meeting place, the Hall of Hewn Stone at the Temple. Caiaphas dispensed with any untrustworthy use of witnesses. Testimony already had been given. However, to appease members not present the night before and to prod the prisoner into convicting himself again, he permitted brief questioning.

"Art thou the Christ? tell us."

"If I tell you, ye will not believe . . . nor let me go,"

he said. Then once more he gave them what they wanted. "Hereafter shall the Son of man sit on the right hand of the power of God."

They pounced on this. "Art thou then the Son of God?"

"Ye say that I am."

Again the associates of Caiaphas stirred up a demonstration of outrage. "What need we any further witness? . . . we ourselves have heard of his own mouth." It worked, slickly, rapidly and positively, as Caiaphas had planned. Again, objections were outvoted or shouted down.

A little later, a throng stood outside the governor's quarters and shouted Jesus to the cross. Caiaphas had completed his difficult and ingeniously calculated operation to secure his power. But it failed.

He himself not long afterward was removed from office. And within forty years, the aristocratic, political-minded Sadducees whose worldly goals he prized and symbolized were shorn of influence in Judaism and replaced by genuinely religious forces. His own elite Sadducean oligarchy, sullied by its cunning and its desperate concern for security, went into oblivion. In his passion for power, Caiaphas had tried to destroy an idea. But instead, the power was dissipated, while the idea won its legions around the earth. Caiaphas was a practical, shrewd little man, but he overlooked one point: Real power resides ultimately not in sly means, but in sound ends. And Caiaphas is remembered, not for saving a nation, but for plotting the death of her most universally beloved son.

17

JUDAS ISCARIOT

". . . behold, the hand of him that betrayeth me . . ."

JUDAS ISCARIOT shuffled along the dark, narrow street. It was near the start of the fourth watch, halfway from midnight to dawn, and only wraiths of conscience peopled the gloom. Judas' unsteady hand fingered the thirty shekels in the purse tied at his girdle. He shuddered.

Why had he done it? he asked himself wretchedly. Why?

He gritted his teeth, anger mingling with hopelessness. The priests—curse their heads—had been highly attentive when he first went to them yesterday with his plan. They had received him gladly, right up to the high priest himself. But now that he had rendered his service, they had cast him aside, spurned him as the others had spurned him. Yea, all of them—John, Peter, Philip and all the rest!

They always had demeaned him, listing him last among the twelve, giving him the menial jobs to do, such as carrying the common purse, tending to collections, bickering over buying provisions. But what had it gained him? No special thanks, no special notice. Nothing!

Among the other disciples he had been like a stranger, an aloof, gruff man from Kerioth, while all the others were Galileans. He never had found warmth for himself among them. He kept his own counsel, except to grumble at extravagances. He often sat apart, his bony face sullen, begrudging the others their congeniality. In his view, they didn't give him enough credit for his knowledge of figures, counting and weighing, or for all the tedious chores he did for them. John—that favorite of the Master's—had even suspected him of stealing from the scanty common fund. Yet they had been through much together, and at times he had tasted the sweet nectar of fellowship. Now all that was ended.

Judas weaved into a fence, and glanced off it. He hunched his neck between his shoulders, floundering on down a dark alleyway. With all his resentment, he also had a dread sense of loss.

For nearly three years, he had given up his merchandising trade to work for the Master, serving him dutifully, carrying out his instructions for distributing money to the poor, managing expenses, awaiting that promised great victory, that rich kingdom in the sun. But it never came. His only reward had been distrust, even by Jesus himself. It was true—the Master had known! Judas' lips twitched, the horror rising in him. He slumped along erratically, not knowing where he was going, or caring, following the dark tunnels of the streets wherever they led.

Months ago when some of the disciples had been assuring Jesus that they would never forsake him, the Master had nodded perceptively. "Have I not chosen you twelve, and one of you is a devil?" He must have known, or guessed, even then.

An urge to run came over Judas. He didn't run, but he did move faster, the slapping of his sandals making hollow echoes against the stone walls, his aimless course pursued by dark shapes and phantom whispers. "Is it I? . . . Is it I?" Yes, it was he.

But he could not change it now. It was all over. The deed was done, the record written in glaring letters, forever.

He had thought that he had solid reasons for his action when he went to the high priest yesterday. His mind had stormed with spite, recklessness and visions of rewards. He felt he had endured enough of their bedraggled little band, wandering the country, consorting with scum, comforting the sickly, the beggars and the wicked. It didn't seem to him that the Master was even practical. Why, only this week, he had let some woman anoint him with three hundred denarii—a year's wages—worth of spikenard perfume. Judas had complained testily that it was a waste, but Jesus had defended her. "Let her alone: against the day of my burying hath she kept this."

Judas had wanted no more sentiment. Enough of this passive waiting! If Jesus actually were the Messiah, he could call down legions of angels to save him from swords, prisons, penalties. If not, he should rightly be exposed.

Judas had wanted action—at once—and his own crucial role in it inflamed him.

The silver the high priest gave him was miserly, about enough to buy a lame slave. It meant little to him, in the fury of his vindictiveness, frustration, loneliness and hunger for prestige. So he had pledged to lead them to the nightly meeting place. Then, his nerves ajangle, he had rejoined the others.

Early last evening they had gathered at a friend's house in a large upper room around a low table spread by the women followers with little salted fish, herbs, roasted lamb, preserved vegetables, sauce and fruit. The Master, in that peculiar way he had of making lowly gestures seem noble, took the washing basin from the servant, wrapped a towel around himself and got down on his knees and washed their feet. He said such acts knitted master and servant together. But then, in a knowing way, he said, "Ye are not all clean." Judas, stretched there on a couch, froze for an instant, but recovered. He decided he must have just imagined that the Master glanced at him when he made the remark.

He was tense and uncomfortable, however, as the meal began. His place was at Jesus' left. John was at Jesus' right and, beyond him, Peter. Judas was glad he didn't have to face those two, or Jesus, either. They had sipped the first cup of wine and just begun to eat when the Master said:

"Verily I say unto you, One of you which eateth with me shall betray me."

Judas flinched, and averted his eyes. Shocked silence

gripped the room for several moments. Then they all began to murmur, wounded, incredulous. Peter nudged John, whispering to him to ask the Master who it could be. Judas, trying to conceal his panic, began concentrating intently on eating. The others, quietly at first and then with rising urgency, began asking, one after another, "Lord, is it I? . . . Is it I? . . . Is it I?"

"It is one of the twelve," Jesus said, "that dippeth with me in the dish."

Judas stuffed his sauce-soaked bread into his mouth, choking. "Master," he forced out weakly, "is it I?"

Jesus glanced at him. "That thou doest, do quickly."

Judas had left at once, tripping over his own mantle as he got up, fleeing outside in a daze of fright. Once away from them, however, his consternation began to subside. None of them had tried to stop him. In fact, they acted unconcerned with his departure, ignoring him as usual.

Certainly they didn't realize his intentions, apparently thinking Jesus had ordered him to go on one of his usual purchasing errands. They wouldn't even miss him. It was a fearsome moment, though. And the Master knew, knew fully, to the very time! A tremor had started deep inside Judas, but he had staved it off by walking rapidly toward the house of Caiaphas.

He couldn't weaken then. He had gone too far. He had committed himself and had to go through with it. He tried to whistle as he hurried along through the early evening, but the notes were blurred and breathy. The others, in a little while, would be singing hymns and Psalms at the close of the meal.

Despite his momentary qualms, everything was going as he had planned. If the Master could be taken by armed men, he must not have the power to usher in any heavenly reign. And Judas—for once—would be an important figure in bringing things to a decision, of ending the hoax, if it were a hoax. Surely the nation's leaders would be in debt to him after this night, and give recognition for his service.

From the house of Caiaphas, he was sent with guards to the Fortress Antonia, where a body of soldiers began forming at once, assembling their gear. Everything had been awaiting the word from Judas. All depended on him. He was the center of this stirring of many men, this movement of forces, this barking of commands and launching of action. His body tingled. He was amazed at the large Roman contingent forming, more than a hundred soldiers, in their short, pleated tunics, over which fitted the tough cuirasses of leather fringed and studded with metal. They adjusted their flashing helmets and strapped on their swords, slapping the weapons against their legs.

A group of chief priests, high dignitaries of the Caiaphas administration, and Temple guards also were there with their staves and bludgeons. It took some time for the detachment to form. By now, the Master and the disciples would be on the mountain outside the city, in the garden of a friend's country house where they often met to pray and talk. Judas set his jaw, his breathing heavy.

At last, a chief priest gave him the signal. They were ready to start. And he was the guide, the main figure, the leader of the expedition. Pointing ahead, like the general of an army, he led them down the hill, out through the city gate, down through the dark valley of Kidron, and across the brook. He walked at the front with the chief Temple officials, and behind came the marching clomp of the soldiers, all of them moving at his bidding. As they climbed the slope toward the Garden of Gethsemane, Judas advised the Temple officials, "Whomsoever I shall kiss, that same is he; take him . . ." A kiss was the customary greeting. Judas, in his new position of authority, added, ". . . lead him away safely."

The torchlights and lanterns made grotesque, leaping shadows on the olive trees and matted ground as they entered the walled garden. It seemed alive and swaying, but with no sign of human beings. The detachment halted. For an instant, Judas scanned about desperately. Then through the trees he caught sight of a white garment, and knew the disciples were there.

He led the Temple officials forward. Jesus stepped forth out of the darkness. "Whom seek ye?"

"Hail, master," Judas said, and kissed him.

Jesus' words cut like a blade. "Judas, betrayest thou the Son of man with a kiss?" Judas glanced nervously at the priests and officials. The soldiers had remained in the rear, cut off by the trees.

Suddenly, the brash Peter came stomping up, drawing a broadsword. He slashed out, cutting off the ear of the high priest's servant, Malchus. The servant screamed. Cringing backward, the officials shouted for the guards and soldiers. But Jesus curbed the violent Peter.

"Put up thy sword . . ." he said. ". . . all they that take the sword shall perish with the sword. . . ." He touched the ear, healing it, and turned to Peter, admonishing him, "Suffer ye thus far. . . . the cup which my Father hath given me, shall I not drink it?"

Just then, the head of the Roman column and guards, with their weapons, moved forward into the clearing. Judas breathed with relief. The Master, confronting the armed force, said with unconcealed irony, "Are ye come out, as against a thief, with swords and with staves to take me? I was daily with you in the temple teaching, and ye took me not . . . but this is your hour, and the power of darkness."

The priests didn't deign to reply, but irascibly motioned the troops forward to seize him. The forbidding array of armed might had sent the disciples skulking away into the shadows, and Judas smiled grimly. They were quitting the Master, too, now that they saw the facts.

Jesus was bound securely, and led away down the hill. Judas tried to rejoin the leaders of the party, but they brushed him aside. Off with you! He hung back a moment, stunned, and then rushed forward again. Perhaps they hadn't noticed who he was. But again they shouldered him aside, not permitting him among them, scorning him. They had paid him. Be off! They were done with him.

He lagged back, a lonely bitterness boiling in him. He stumbled along in the bushes beside the troops, falling farther behind. Yet he kept on following them. He had nowhere else to go. The tremors began in his body again, and this time they swelled into a physical shaking.

He lurked outside the houses of Annas and Caiaphas, and saw Jesus mocked and beaten. He hadn't expected such brutality. Jesus was no outlaw. He was a good man. Then came the harsh denunciations of Caiaphas, the clamorous verdict—death! Judas staggered away into the night. The full weight of his deed came down on him. Dismay struck like a bolt in his heart.

All night now, he had wandered the streets, stumbling over the refuse and the beggars sleeping on the pavement. Around and through the lifeless city, and back again, he moved without cause or direction through the silent darkness, his eyes unseeing, his soul a volcano of tormented memories.

Why? Why? Why had he done it? The kindness of Jesus, all the days and hardships they had surmounted together, sifted through him. He mumbled incoherently, a retching in his throat. His foot collided with a stack of wood, and there was a swift, dark movement. A cat dashed away yowling.

In the dawn, he saw the soldiers at the fortress laying out the crossbeams for an execution. He made his way to the Temple, his body numb, his eyes glazed and bleak. He sought to return the silver, whimpering, "I have sinned in that I have betrayed the innocent blood."

They laughed at him. "What is that to us?"

Judas flung the thirty coins on the Temple floor. He stood there like a dead man, a terrible revulsion in him, as the coins rolled and scattered to rest on the smooth floor. He walked dully away. Outside he vomited.

Judas, the archtraitor, had gained nothing, nothing but a torture in his soul and a quaking in his bones. Yet he must in some respects have been a man of gallant hopes and daring adventure to have served so long the cause of Jesus. But he lost his way.

The Temple priests, unable to use the money he had returned in the Temple treasury because it was "blood money" used it instead to buy a potter's field, Akeldama, "the field of blood," for burying paupers.

Judas hanged himself. His body was cut down and thrown headlong into the field, where it burst and spattered over the ground, the end of a glum and lonely man whose name meant "serpent."

18

PETER

"And Peter remembered the word of Jesus . . .
And he went out, and wept bitterly."

I**T SEEMED IMPOSSIBLE. But it had happened.
Like water seeping into a storm-lashed ship, fear
had crept through his body, and the great, indom-
itable Peter had blurted out his momentous lie. "I
know not this man . . ."**

Now the words beat in his mind like the hammering
of an angry sea. "I know him not . . . I know him not . . .
I know him not." Three times, with rising truculence, he
had said it; three times, with weakness breeding weakness,
he had blared out his denial of the Lord.

Then he had begun to curse and swear, hating himself,
hating the world around him, hating the sound of that
cock crowing in the distance, a cock in Jerusalem where
no cocks should be kept, but a cock crowing all the same.
It had sounded like far-off bitter laughter.

In the trembling, ominous dawn, as the hooting guards

led their bound victim away, Peter sat hunched on a stoop, his face a guttered mask, sobbing convulsively.

The "rock" had turned into sand.

Sick with shame, he plunged in thought back to the moment when the Master had first given him that name. He heard again Jesus' probing questions, heard his own swift, ringing declaration of faith: "Thou art the Christ, the Son of the living God."

Peter covered his face with his hands, his nails digging into the flesh. What a desecration, what a travesty he had made of the mighty commission the Master had given him then!

MATT
16:18

"And I say also unto thee, That thou art Peter, and upon this rock I will build my church; and the gates of hell shall not prevail against it."

But he, Peter, the big, brusque, stalwart leader of the twelve, had collapsed like rotted timber when the gale struck, when the peril came, when the club-wielding soldiers swarmed into the garden and tied up Christ like a thief.

With the others, he had fled in craven alarm, a flimsy reed in the tempest. Then, furtively he had followed to the scene of the Master's night interrogation before the councilors of the Sanhedrin at the palace of the high priest. Peter had slipped unnoticed into the hall with some servants and soldiers, warming themselves by a fireplace. But suspicious eyes had turned on him. And there, in hostile surroundings, he had cringed before the accusing questions.

"Art not thou also one of this man's disciples?" they kept asking.

"I am not . . . I know him not."

"Of a truth . . . Did not I see thee in the garden with him?"

"I know not the man."

"Surely thou also art one of them . . . thou art a Galilean . . . thy speech bewrayeth thee."

"Man, I know not what thou sayest." Peter swore vehemently. "I know him not."

Just at that moment, across the room, the bruised, disheveled Jesus had turned and gazed at him silently. The look, hurt but unsurprised, drove through Peter like a flight of arrows. Unseeingly, he fled the hall.

Only a few hours earlier, when they all supped in the upper room and Jesus spoke forebodingly of coming death and of Peter denying him, the impetuous fisherman had sworn he'd never do it—never!

"Though I should die with thee, yet will I not deny thee," he had vowed. "Lord, I am ready to go with thee, both into prison, and to death."

But Jesus had known, had measured him, had seen through the blustering inanities of man. "Verily I say unto thee, That this day, even in this night, before the cock crow twice, thou shalt deny me thrice." And so he had, and so that screeching cock had flung its scorn at him across the dark house-tops.

He had failed miserably, anxious only for his own life, a weakling with no sap in him, like the swaying weeds of the sea. An inconstant wind, as fickle as the abruptly changing moods of the Galilee lake. He had disowned the truth the Lord had given him, the trust that he had possessed.

Oh, man of little faith, sounding your own trumpet of hollow courage, your vaunted high resolves crashing on the hidden shoals of human frailty! Peter stared numbly at the ground. At length he rose shakily, and plodded after the sounds of the guard across the lower city and up the hill toward the Hall of Hewn Stone, with its dungeon prison. Revulsion at his facile promises swam through him, a vileness in his throat.

Back when they were at Caesarea Philippi, far up at the headwaters of the Jordan, where Jesus first told them that he must suffer and die for mankind, Peter had said it mustn't happen, that he wouldn't let it happen: "Be it far from thee, Lord: this shall not be unto thee."

But Jesus had gauged him then, too, and knew him. ". . . thou savourest not the things that be of God, but the things that be of men."

Big, bluff, red-bearded Peter! Driving, large-hearted, unceremonious—the man to whom Jesus had entrusted "the keys of the kingdom." But a man? No, a sounding shell. Peter slumped along, gripping his chest with his arms, as if he could smother the guilt.

He had been right when Jesus first came to him there at the fishing boat with his brother, Andrew. He had felt at once he wasn't worthy. He had fallen to his knees, mortified. "Depart from me; for I am a sinful man, O Lord." But Jesus had taken him despite himself. "Follow me, and I will make you fishers of men. . . . henceforth thou shalt catch men."

Gratefully, eagerly then, Peter had gone, throwing his whole being into the cause, giving his lusty vigor and fealty to Jesus. He had previously been touched by the preaching of John the Baptist, and so the summons of Jesus had lifted him up in startled elation, in a forceful, unreserved allegiance.

His mind choked with memories—of the lilt that had sprung in his heart at the Master's sure guidance, of the fresh, singing vista of life opened to him, the miracles of love, kindness, humility—they bought more than gold. ". . . he that cometh to me shall never hunger; and he that believeth on me shall never thirst."

The voice came back to him like a never-dying echo. ". . . seek, and ye shall find; knock, and it shall be opened unto you . . . Thou shalt love the Lord they God . . . [and] thy neighbour as thyself. . . . ye shall know the truth, and the truth shall make you free."

The wonder of it all had saturated the rustic Peter, captured his life, taken him away from his work, his home and his wife in Capernaum, given him, as he walked with Jesus, a sense of mission that was both new and over-whelming.

Peter remembered the time that he and James and John, only those three, had been taken by Jesus to the top of a mountain. There in the misty heights, such a radiance as had never been seen before came over Jesus, and the command descended from the heavens, "This is my be-loved Son, in whom I am well pleased; hear ye him." They had heard him; they had believed him. But now they had abandoned him.

Peter reached the top of the hill, and leaned against an outer wall of the Temple.

At times, all of them had bungled and misunderstood, as in their petty, foolhardy arguments over who would be first in the Lord's kingdom, their fright in the storm at sea, and Peter's vain attempt to walk on water, only to lose heart and sink, crying out, "Lord, save me." And Jesus had reached out and saved him. Oh, thou of little faith! Why did you doubt? Why did you fail? Why did you bend and grovel?

"He that loveth his life shall lose it . . ." It was true, it was true! In the moment of trial he had hoarded his life, clutched it for its own sake, and thereby rendered it nothing. "For what is a man profited, if he shall gain the whole world, and lose his own soul?"

Oh Lord, Lord! Peter threw back his head, hitting it against the stone wall, and the image of himself rose bloodless and skeletal. ". . . whosoever shall be ashamed of me and of my words, of him shall the Son of man be ashamed . . . And if a house be divided against itself, that house cannot stand. . . ."

Even at the final supper, when Jesus had taken a towel and basin and started to wash their feet, the impulsive Peter had protested. He loved the Master too much to let him do that. "Thou shalt never wash my feet." But when Jesus explained that mutual service made them part of each other, Peter had turned enthusiastically to the other extreme. "Lord, not my feet only, but also my hands and my head."

How empty his fervent devotion seemed now. Often in the past, when they floundered, Jesus had been there to set them straight, to put their values aright, to shore up their convictions. Then, like the sealing of a bond at the meal last night, Jesus had divided the loaf and shared it with them, calling it his body "which is given for you: this do in remembrance of me," and passed the wine, his blood "shed for many. . . . Drink ye all of it . . ." You, he said, are the light of the world. But almost at once they had dashed the pledge to shame. In the Garden of Gethsemane, before the traitor came, they had proved what weaklings they were. "My soul is exceeding sorrowful, even unto death," Jesus had said hoarsely, "tarry ye here, and watch with me." He had walked apart from them a little distance and fallen on his knees beside a rock to pray. "O my Father, if it be possible, let this cup pass from me: never-theless not as I will, but as thou wilt." He prayed on and on, the words low and tortured, an endless hurting in the night, but even as he prayed, they had dozed. ". . . could ye not watch with me one hour?" They had hung their heads. Then came the armed mob to seize him, and after Peter's last futile gesture with his broadsword, they had run. All of them. Run and cowered and denied.

Peter's head hung heavy, his body leaden, his eyes red and dry. In the gray daybreak, objects seemed to appear and fade, appear and fade. For him, the night didn't end as the sun rose that day.

Whither now, "rock"? Back to the nets? Back to

the Galilee lake to cast for the gray mullet and the blenny before the Jordan carries them down to death in the salt of the Dead Sea? No longer a "fisher of men"?

Once before, ever so long ago it seemed now, when trouble darkened the way, when some of Jesus' followers had left him, Jesus had asked, "Will ye also go away?" Dimly, deep in his grief, Peter remembered the answer he had given: "Lord, to whom shall we go? thou hast the words of eternal life."

Then it came back to him, faintly at first, ever so faintly, but with a rising beat, the Master's unworried knowledge: "All of ye will fall away . . . the spirit indeed is willing, but the flesh is weak. . . . Let not your heart be troubled, neither let it be afraid." The words—the significance—pounded in Peter's veins. ". . . ye shall be scattered . . . and shall leave me alone: and yet I am not alone, because the Father is with me. . . .

"It is expedient for you that I go away . . . I go to prepare a place for you. . . . ye shall weep and lament . . . but your sorrow shall be turned into joy. . . . Abide in me, and I in you. . . . I am the vine, ye are the branches . . . I have chosen you, and ordained you . . . continue ye in my love. . . . In the world ye shall have tribulation: but be of good cheer; I have overcome the world."

A great warmth flowed over Peter. He remembered he had once asked Jesus how many times a man's sins could be forgiven—seven times? No, not just seven times, Jesus had said, but "seventy times seven." A love, a forgiveness, without limit, reaching to infinity. "Peace I leave with you, my peace I give unto you . . ." Peter lifted his head, a world ahead of him, still to win. Even in his ignominy, the Lord understood and pardoned, a Lord undaunted by denials and death.

So, too, Simon Peter—Cephas, the rock—mastered his own storm, and the Lord's assurance abode in him. Before Jesus departed the earth, he spoke again with his grand apostle: "Simon, son of Jonas, lovest thou me?"

"Yea, Lord; thou knowest that I love thee."

"Feed my lambs."

Twice, Jesus repeated the question, and Peter, contrite, dedicated to the marrow of his being, his fervor resounding as it always did and always would, said, "Lord, thou knowest all things; thou knowest that I love thee."

"Feed my sheep."

Three times he had denied, caught in the unseen undertows of the flesh, but three times, and many times that, he affirmed his huge devotion, steadfast in his consecration to the kingdom of the spirit appointed to him.

". . . my flesh shall rest in hope . . ." he said. "Silver and gold have I none; but such as I have give I . . . the times of refreshing shall come . . ."

A rocklike pillar of faith, he spread a foundation for Christ that stretched across three continents, braving prisons and attacks, casting his wide net for men in countries of Asia, Africa and Europe. It is said that he himself finally was crucified by a roadside pine near Rome, head downward at his request in deference to his Lord, the friend who had told him, "Greater love hath no man than this, that a man lay down his life for his friends."

19

NICODEMUS

"There was a man of the Pharisees . . .
a ruler of the Jews . . ."

EALTHY, OLD Nicodemus watched the clamorous mob surging along the street, shoving their victim along before them. He fingered his staff fretfully, clasping and unclasping it, and his lips moved without making any sound. He wanted to do something, but what could he do?

He hobbled along after the crowd, pausing occasionally to shake his stick at them. He couldn't quite keep up, but he could follow the sound of their course and he knew they were taking the rabbi of Galilee to Herod's palace. The winds of iniquity are let loose, he grieved. Falsehood sits in high places. Fear rides across the city and truth is trampled in the street. They mean to kill the rabbi, Jesus. Nicodemus bent forward as he walked, stabbing with his staff, and his gray beard flowed over his shoulders. He had heard the demands for death at the praetorium, and now the Roman governor was sending Jesus to be judged by Herod Antipas, here from Galilee for the coming Passover.

The mob turned a corner and was out of sight. Nicodemus moved on down the hill, following the narrow streets southward across the city. Pedestrians shuttled around him, and tradesmen dangled their wares before him, but he saw them only dimly. He kept going, a burning distress driving him on.

For a year he had been aware of official antagonism to the unorthodox rabbi, Jesus; had seen it slowly gather force. As an elder member of the Sanhedrin and a propertied citizen of Jerusalem, Nicodemus had tried in vain to counteract it, knowing that, unchecked, it would lead only to grave injustice. But the majority had ignored his pleas because he was old and the summit of his power had passed; because he was not alert to the "present peril." A young councilor had scoffed accusingly, "Art thou also of Galilee?" Others had turned and looked at him, their eyes speculative and suspicious. Could a man no longer speak his mind? Nicodemus, in the wisdom of his years, had been ashamed of the fever of distrust sweeping his country.

He hesitated now at the corner of the street of the cheesemakers, not sure which way to go; then his sense of direction came back, and he plodded on, not knowing exactly why, not actually thinking he could do anything, but going on nevertheless, his conscience burdened by helplessness and shame.

It had been several months ago, at the time the high priest and his agents had initiated their plan to arrest Jesus, that Nicodemus first tried to stop them. Despite his quiet, retiring role in affairs of state, he had spoken up, protesting the illegality of ordering an arrest without a hearing or even a charge. "Doth our law judge any man before it hear him, and know what he doeth?" he had protested. But all it had gained was irritated scorn and the snide innuendo about his own loyalty.

It is weakness that breeds these things, he thought, weakness and fear. It is fear of the powerful, and the weakness of their tools of conformity—the timid, the indifferent, the acquiescers, the perjurers and rumormongers. In his mind, Nicodemus could not shake off the scenes of last night and early this morning, the abusive frenzy in which the Sanhedrin had demanded death for Jesus. None of it had been right. None of it had been equitable. The judges had acted as if all balance had left them.

No definite charge had been brought. Some of the court had taken part in the plot to arrest Jesus, in prosecuting him, in supplying witnesses. All this had violated Jewish law. Legally, two witnesses testifying in accord were required to convict a man of even a petty offense, but the witnesses last night had provided nothing but discrepancies. Members of the council, the high priest himself, had goaded and hectored the defenseless rabbi, determined to bully something, anything, out of him with which to concoct a crime, despite strict Jewish laws protecting a man against self-incrimination. The whole thing was a disgrace.

Nicodemus jabbed his stick hard against the stones, sending a shock through his arm. Moreover, the law forbade holding a criminal trial at night. One point they had observed, partially. They had tried to make it appear that the required day had elapsed between trial and verdict by calling another session this morning. Yet how false, how hollow all of it had been. Council members had been like stubble in a whirlwind, swept along by their fear of the rabbi's criticism, his threat to their entrenched positions. There was no stopping them, then or anytime. Nicodemus and Joseph of Arimathea, possibly others, had opposed them. But their objections had been lost in the uproar.

After the judgment had been rendered, the soldiers and even some of the councilors had buffeted the bound Jesus about, pummeling him on the face and body. Some guards had tied a blindfold on him and hit him, taunting, "Prophesy unto us, thou Christ, Who is he that smote thee?" Through it all, knocked about there in the council chamber, Jesus had never uttered a word of anger or entreaty, submitting to it all in sorrowful silence.

Nicodemus knew that many of his fellow Pharisees supported Jesus, but only in secret lest they be put out of the synagogue. Fear had depleted them, too, had even allied some of those devout, learned men in the scheme against Jesus with those they normally opposed—the hardheaded, worldly Sadducees and the Herodians, flaunting their pagan dress and customs. The fear made strange bedfellows.

Down the street ahead of him, Nicodemus could see the waiting mob outside the gates of Herod's palace. His breath came jerkily from the haste of his walk, but he pressed on toward the edge of the crowd, muttering imprecations against them. They probably would not listen. Mobs did not listen. But he had to try. He had to do something, even though there was nothing he could do.

He reached the edge of the restive crowd. They were staring toward the palace gate. He touched first one man and then another with his stick to draw their attention, and started to exhort them to reason and justice. The men looked at him stolidly. Then abruptly a collective murmur went up from the crowd, and all peered excitedly toward the palace, pressing against each other. Nicodemus kept pleading, but none heard. He moved among them, still trying to gain their ears, but their clatter smothered his voice, and their shoving jostled him about.

He saw that the soldiers were bringing Jesus back through the gates of the palace, pushing and hazing him along. He wore a purple cloak now, hung on him in obvious mockery. The soldiers drove him up the street, back the way they had come, and the crowd turned and followed at their heels, their clamor growing louder as they moved. The word passed among them that Herod Antipas was sending the culprit back to Pilate.

Nicodemus turned this way and that, trying to detain some of them, clasping at a sleeve here, urging there, spreading his hands in appeal for them to stay and hear him, but they surged on, passing the old man by, infected with the mass contagion.

For a moment, Nicodemus put his head in his hands, overcome by futility and weariness. Then he rallied again and started after the retreating mob, swinging his stick at them threateningly, crying out in broken syllables. Sweat poured down his wrinkled cheeks, and he tried to speed his gait, but fatigue and despair bore down on him.

There is no honor, he murmured, and no justice. No Moses or David to brandish the rod of God. Unless it be this rabbi of Galilee, and the tides of deceit and fear race through the city, dragging him to his death.

Nicodemus, as a long-time leader of his people, had not leaped to any quick conclusions about Jesus. To make sure of his ground and avoid leading others astray, he had made a nighttime call on the rabbi when he had been in Jerusalem the year before to inquire into his teaching and healing genius. Jesus had said then that a man must be "born again" in order to enter the kingdom of God, and Nicodemus had asked, puzzled, "How can a man be born when he is old?" Jesus had explained that he meant a re-birth of the spirit, not the flesh, an inner freshening that exposed a man's ordinary arrogance and made him like a child, knowing he is small, yet exuberantly strong because of his assurance that the Father cares for him. And then he had said something about God's so caring for men that he had sent his Son—in man's likeness—to suffer the burden of men's sins, and thereby show the way to eternity for all who accepted him.

Still Nicodemus had been perplexed, and Jesus had said it was hard to grasp a spiritual truth—that it was like a wind moving through the workings of God, that you couldn't see it or tell where it came from or where it went

—but you knew it was present. " . . . light is come into the world . . ." Jesus had told him. ". . . he that doeth truth cometh to the light . . ."

Now Nicodemus trudged along the street, the memory a stabbing nostalgia within him, the mob long gone from sight. He knew Jesus must be from God, knew it with an overwhelming certainty that came on him he knew not how, untraceable as the wind. He pushed on across an open square, his fingers numb from grasping his staff. He came to a fountain and, steadying himself with the staff, sank down on the side of it, a vertigo in his head, his limbs weak and shaky.

Far up the hill, he again heard the dim cries of "Crucify." The light is come, he thought, but they quench the light, suppress the truth. Suppression is always the weapon of fear. But truth would rise again!

Slowly the fluttering of his heart steadied, and his strength began to return. He sat there, with the gush of the fountain clear and melodious in the deserted square, and the words that Jesus had spoken to him that night long ago flowed back over him like soothing waters:

"For God so loved the world, that he gave his only begotten Son, that whosoever believeth in him should not perish, but have everlasting life. For God sent not his Son into the world to condemn the world; but that the world through him might be saved."

In a little while, the mob again moved along the street away from the judgment seat of Pontius Pilate and toward the hill of Calvary. This time Nicodemus did not shake his stick, did not shout his condemnation. He could not stop them. They could not be stopped.

The forces of the times prevented that. He was not sure who or what was responsible. No single agency or group or man could be blamed. Even Jesus had foreseen his fate, and moved toward it, ready to die, offering his life because of men's sins. Only sin alone could be blamed, men's continual blundering, their perverse confusion, their fears and cruelties.

No, Nicodemus could not stop it. But one thing he could do. He stood up, his frail, old back straight and determined. He knew Jesus' friends had abandoned him in the heat of danger, but not all would forsake him—not Nicodemus—not this rich, scholarly, old Jewish leader.

Casting caution aside, he would present himself later in the day at Pilate's court. A colleague, Joseph of Arimathea, another wealthy Jewish leader and member of the Sanhedrin, also would be there. Both, jeopardizing their standing by showing partisanship for the condemned revolutionary, would ask permission to give Jesus a decent burial. And Pilate, cynically surprised, would grant it.

Joseph had for the purpose a tomb he had prepared for himself. Nicodemus would bring a hundred pounds of aromatic myrrh and aloes juices to sprinkle in the burial linen to retard decomposition. Together, these two men and their servants, after the trial and killing were over, would take Jesus' lifeless body down from the cross and carry it to Joseph's "long home." Nicodemus, the courageous old man who spoke up for Jesus when most of his regular friends deserted him, could do something, after all.

Tradition has it that Nicodemus later was baptized by John and Peter, consequently deprived of his office and banished, an inquiring, philosophical old man in whom truth could not be suppressed by mob hysteria or servile fears.

20

PILATE

"And the whole multitude of them arose, and led him unto Pilate."

FLANKED BY ATTENDANTS, Pontius Pilate stepped out onto the balcony of the Fortress Antonia. At the appearance of the Roman governor, the sentries at the gate came to alert attention, their spears at their sides. A dying dawn breeze rippled the folds of his toga as he surveyed the scene below him. A mass of people fanned out from the arched gateway of the stone court. In front of them huddled a group of ornately garbed priests with their prisoner, bound in ropes.

A wisp of cynicism played at Pilate's lips as he lifted his toga and descended the stairs to a landing just above them. Considering the early hour, the high priest had produced quite a little turnout for his drama.

A portable tribunal seat had been placed on the landing. Pilate sat down, folded his arms and peered down urbanely at the priestly delegation. "What accusation bring ye against this man?" This had been Caiaphas' idea. Let him explain it.

There was a hurried consultation among the priests. Then Caiaphas raised his head and said, "If he were not a malefactor, we would not have delivered him up unto thee."

Pilate's eyes narrowed, and the lordly tolerance he had assumed for the occasion deserted him. If they wouldn't detail the charges, he wouldn't be bothered with the piddling affair. "Take ye him," Pilate snapped, with a gesture of dismissal. ". . . judge him according to your law." He rose abruptly to leave them.

But before his foot touched the first stair, the words from below stopped him. "It is not lawful for us to put any man to death." A bit startled, Pilate turned back slowly. So they wanted an execution. This was news to him. A sticky business. He'd been willing to furnish troops to arrest the dissenter, on the ground that it would ease local friction, but he had direct responsibility for any death sentence. And the emperor might well demand an accounting. Pilate stood there, tapping his chin with his forefinger. Already his methods had drawn scowls from Rome for being too ruthless. He didn't mind spilling blood himself, but he had to keep Tiberius satisfied, as well as placate these obstinate natives with their religious eccentricities.

From down below, someone called out: "We found this fellow perverting the nation . . . saying that he himself is Christ a King."

Pilate grimaced. For his own political protection, he'd have to look into the thing. He spoke to an aide, ordering him to have the prisoner brought into the governor's quarters. He climbed the stairs and went back inside and paced about the room.

He knew too well that petty religious squabbles could flare into serious disorder among these monotheistic Jews. He had to be careful, shrewd. Firmness but conciliation —that was the emperor's command. Not that the fellow's life mattered.

But ambition burned hard in Pilate, whose ancestors had risen from slavery. He knew that diplomatic mastery over these troublesome Judeans was the key to power. Personally, he had no use for justice—a plague on it! But he had to play the game, if he expected to keep in good grace with his superiors. Not a few procurators of this province, four of them in twenty years, had been recalled to Rome and divested of office for clashes with the Jews, including Pilate's predecessor, Valerius Gratus. Despite some turbulent moments, Pilate had managed to hang on for nearly four years now.

The tramp of boots sounded outside the door, and an officer prodded the prisoner into the apartment. Pilate strolled over toward him, examining him distastefully, looking him up and down.

He was a tall, strong-featured Jew, badly roughed up, though, with abrasions marring his face and neck. His captors had worked him over rather thoroughly. But he seemed harmless enough, with a calm, unprotesting manner. Probably just another of these religious spouters.

"Art thou the King of the Jews?" Pilate asked sardonically. The country was full of vagabond soothsayers with fool's dreams and impractical notions.

There was a subtle sting in this one's reply, however. "Sayest thou this thing of thyself, or did others tell it thee of me?"

Pilate held his temper and strolled across the room to a stand with a bowl of fruit on it. He popped a grape into his mouth, then turned back to the prisoner. ". . . Thine own nation and the chief priests have delivered thee unto me: what hast thou done?"

The man had some visionary answer. "My kingdom is not of this world . . ." Plainly, he was just a paltry mystic—with nothing to do with the weighty matter of runing the actual world.

Pilate smiled condescendingly. "Art thou a king then?"

The prisoner didn't see the humor in the question. ". . . To this end was I born," he said evenly, "and for this cause came I into the world, that I should bear witness unto the truth. . . ."

Pilate shrugged. "What is truth?" A chimera, an idle fancy. Pleased by his own sage realism, he left the room and descended the stairs to the outdoor judgment seat.

The crowd quieted.

"I find," Pilate announced, "no fault in this man."

An uproar of protests rose from the crowd. "He stirreth up the people, teaching throughout all Jewry, beginning from Galilee to this place." The cries grew louder and more strident. Infuriated, Pilate again retreated to his quarters, but the commotion still reached him.

The rabble! Those priests, rubbed raw by their waning authority, were behind this vulgar display, trying to demonstrate their strength, and force him to yield to their ultimata. This prisoner clearly was just a scapegoat, a pawn to revive the issue of Rome's curb on their punitive powers. Nonetheless, the crowd's temper disturbed Pilate. Once before, a mass protest against his use of funds from the Temple treasury to build an aqueduct to Jerusalem had led to widespread slaughter. His troops had had to hack down a swarm of pious rioters. Again, when he had ignored the prohibition of the Pax Romana against offending native religions by affixing imperial images to military standards, he had stirred up a six-day melee. Instead of appreciating the gesture, Tiberius had sent a reprimand. The emperor brooked no brutality, no treason! Even when Pilate had hung some gilded shields inscribed with the emperor's name in the Jerusalem praetorium, the action had caused a native tempest, and Rome had sent a mandate to remove the shields. Indecision tore at Pilate. Rome—the astute mistress! Would that the great Tiberius himself had to deal with this Galilean.

Suddenly the name, "Galilean," ignited a crafty idea in Pilate. He could turn the prisoner over to Herod Antipas, the puppet king of the prisoner's home province of Galilee. Herod also had come to Jerusalem for the Passover period.

Pilate gave instructions to the guards, and they started off with their battered prisoner. The crowd outside the gate followed them. Pilate grinned, self-satisfied. He picked up the cluster of grapes, dropped to a couch, and leisurely nibbled at the fruit. Not only had he circumvented Caiaphas and his mob of throaty actors, but he had cultivated amenities with this grumpy little neighboring king. Antipas had been unfriendly lately, and this would smooth his feathers.

Almost always, Pilate ran into difficulties on his stays in Jerusalem during the big festivals. As a precautionary policy, he customarily shifted his headquarters here during such periods from his regular palace at Caesarea, about a hundred miles to the north. He arrived with a troop of cavalry to keep down disorders. It appeared that he had disposed of the current nuisance with profit and aplomb all around. Tiberius would applaud his cleverness. Stretched there on the couch, Pilate luxuriated, admiring the hues and texture of each grape before he consumed it.

The fortress here, adjoining the northwest corner of the Temple, provided a commanding view of the city. Its facilities, with baths, carpeted apartments, sun porches and well-provisioned basement storerooms offered adequate comforts. Pilate had brought his wife, Claudia Procula, with him this spring. He assumed she was still in bed. He lay back, rolled his eyes toward the ceiling and stretched his arms, yawning. A delightful day.

Indistinctly at first and then with increasing volume, he heard the noise of the crowd. They must be coming back! He got to his feet, annoyed, and strode back out onto the balcony. They still had their prisoner, dressed now as a jest in royal purple. Pilate went back inside to summon his aides.

An officer entered, explaining that Herod Antipas had been gratified to examine the prisoner, having long been curious about him, but, considering him a mere buffoon, had treated him accordingly. The king therefore was returning him for Pilate's pleasure, with warm salutations to the procurator.

Pilate swore silently. He swept back outside and sat down in the curule chair, glowering at the assemblage. Fanatics, all of them! He need not yield to this Caiaphas; the high priest held office by Pilate's confirmation! Their very refusal to enter the "heathen" court—it would defile them—was an insult. Pilate raised his hand. "Ye have brought this man unto me, as one that perverteth the people," he intoned sternly. ". . . behold, I, having examined him before you, have found no fault in this man . . . no, nor yet Herod: for I sent you to him; and, lo, nothing worthy of death is done unto him. I will therefore chastise him, and release him."

Again the stormy outburst assailed his ears, and the priests smacked their foreheads in chagrin. Pilate reddened, his eyes darting about nervously. Then a timely stroke of genius, a new stratagem, came to him.

To pardon one criminal was a Passover custom. Certainly not even this partisan mob would want to free the vile Barabbas, a murderer and a rebel. Pilate raised his hand. "Whom will ye that I release unto you? Barabbas, or Jesus which is called Christ?"

The answer dumbfounded him. "Barabbas."

Pilate sank deeper into his chair, pulling at his lips with clammy fingers. As he debated uncertainly and the crowd milled noisily on the pavement, an assistant handed him a note—in his wife's handwriting. "Have thou nothing to do with that just man," it said, "for I have suffered many things this day in a dream because of him."

Angrily Pilate crumpled the note in his fist. What did Claudia know of rule? Even though her kinship with the imperial family had advanced his career, he didn't intent to abdicate to a woman. What did she know of keeping these superstitious natives pacified? She was about as spirit-haunted as they were, always mulling over her star charts, dream theories and workings of the gods. He should have left her in Caesarea. The only god was the size of your legions!

He stood up, fuming. "What shall I do then with Jesus . . . ?"

"Crucify him."

The combined lungpower hit him like a blast.

"Why, what evil hath he done?" Pilate argued, faltering. "I have found no cause of death in him: I will therefore chastise him, and let him go."

Back came the crashing roar of humanity. "Crucify him. Crucify."

So be it! Pilate stormed back through the curtains, but once inside he wavered again. He didn't mind killing the fellow. Not at all. Yet he had to consider the possible repercussions and his own fortunes. That was what bedeviled him. He decided he'd just have the man flogged, as he had said, and see if that wouldn't appease the yammerers.

He ordered Jesus brought inside the Lithostrotos and taken into an inner cell, where he was stripped and chained to a post. A guard laid on with a three-thonged scourge, tipped with heavy metal and bone. The regulation number of blows, according to Jewish law, was thirty-nine, but Rome imposed no limit, and the guard continued until his arm gave out, the solid whip ends whirring through the air and slamming against the body in a steady rhythm. This, Pilate thought, should tame the "king." At the end, the prisoner sagged semiconscious, his back a raw mass of bleeding stripes. A soldier doused him with water. Then, for amusement, other soldiers wove a loop of thorn stems and pressed it down on the man's head as a crown to go with the purple robe. They put a stick in his hand for a scepter, doubling up with laughter. "Hail, King of the Jews!" they guffawed, bowing. Some of them slapped him and spit in his face. Another jerked the stick from him and whacked him with it.

Satisfied, Pilate returned to the outer platform. "Behold," he informed the mob, "I bring him forth to you, that ye may know that I find no fault in him." As the soldiers brought out Jesus, bloody and staggering, the crowd hummed. Pilate smiled. He had done an impressive job. "Behold," he said, "the man!"

Then pandemonium broke loose again. "Crucify him." The sight of the beaten victim seemed to stimulate more fury than before. "Crucify him."

Pilate had gone as far as he knew how in trying to

stay on two sides of the fence at the same time. The conflict overcame him. "Take ye him, and crucify him," he shouted. Then he repeated feebly, " . . . I find no fault in him."

The governor's loss of self-control brought a contrasting lull, pointedly mocking, over the crowd. A priest spoke up authoritatively. "We have a law, and by our law he ought to die, because he made himself the Son of God."

Pilate, his mind swamped by confusion, withdrew to his quarters again. He asked that the prisoner be brought to him once more and in a state of high agitation demanded, "Whence art thou? . . . knowest thou not that I have power to crucify thee, and have power to release thee?"

The prisoner, looking like a casualty of battle, swayed there silent a few moments, then said with great weariness, "Thou couldest have no power at all against me, except it were given thee from above . . ."

It solved nothing to talk to the man. Pilate, his morale completely broken, dragged himself back out onto the balcony and once more made a halfhearted, cajoling appeal for clemency.

But the mob persisted. A priest shouted scathingly, "If thou let this man go, thou art not Caesar's friend: whosoever maketh himself a king speaketh against Caesar."

Pilate quailed. The idea of dishonoring the name of Caesar sent trickles of fear along his spine. If such word ever got to Rome, he'd be finished. These demonstrators made it look as if they were more patriotic than the governor himself.

"Shall I crucify your King?" His voice squeaked.

"Away with him . . . We have no king but Caesar . . . Crucify him."

Pilate had no objections to taking a life, to slaying Jesus, but he wanted to avoid the consequences. He was willing to mete out death, but wished to shirk the responsibility. So he acted now, not from principle but from self-interest. He had a basin of water brought out, and dipped his hands in it. "I am innocent of the blood of this just person," he said. Then, in the prime, weaseling collapse of integrity that sent Jesus to the cross, he issued the official orders for the execution:

"See ye to it," he croaked.

The purple robe was removed from the prisoner, and his own garments put back on him. Pilate directed a centurion to form the crucifixion detail. Lifting his toga, he walked sedately back up to his apartment, the finished hypocrite, whose pretended honor cloaked nothing but expediency, a weak, vain, and vacillating man, concealing his clear responsibility for the infamous verdict.

He had ruled for death, and denied the blame. He had paraded his innocence even as he decreed the crime. He had befouled justice as he washed his hands. Fifth of the Roman procurators of Judea, he later was recalled to Rome for excessive brutality in putting down a Samaritan religious disorder. In disgrace, tradition says, he committed suicide.

21

PRETONIUS

*"Now when the centurion saw what
was done, he glorified God . . ."*

THREE OF THEM TODAY. A pathetic lot they were, especially one of them. Officer Pretonius jammed on his buckler, spoke sharply to his four-man detail. "Get them started."

He motioned to the herald, who stepped off bearing the tablet with the orders of execution ahead of the condemned prisoners. The disabled one—he looked badly hurt—would never make it. Pretonius muttered an oath.

The fellow swayed under the weight of the eighty-pound crossbeam. Blood soaked through the back of his robe. Obviously he had been severely flogged—probably cuffed about all night without rest. Some jester had put a "king's" crown on him, plaited of thorns.

Pretonius was not amused. Just before he took charge, he had noticed a cluster of the fortress guard hounding the man, spitting on him, striking his face with a switch, bowing and snickering. They had stopped abruptly as Pretonius approached.

But the man must have been harshly used, even before then. His eyes were bruised. Whip cuts showed on his face. He staggered painfully under his burden, stumbling on the paving stones as the procession moved down the hill from the fortress, straining to keep going.

Then he fell, the heavy beam thudding on the pavement. A shrill laugh came from somewhere. Pretonius flashed a wicked look toward the sound. He barked at a soldier, "Get a bystander to carry that beam!" A startled citizen was conscripted for the task.

As the formation moved ahead again, Pretonius roved up and down beside it, getting it in order. An escort guard marched at the rear of the execution party.

Neither of the other two victims had been scourged, and they handled their beams without trouble.

Across the teeming city, a wide-eyed, excited throng trailed the procession. Some women pressed in close to the maimed prisoner, wailing bitterly. "Daughters of Jerusalem," he told them, "weep not for me, but weep for yourselves, and for your children. . . ."

Pretonius shook his head, puzzled. How could the fellow pity the living when he was about to die? The man was a peculiar one—submissive, clean-limbed, with a wise, kindly face, marked with sorrow. Nothing at all like the two truculent bandits who walked beside him. Someone said he was thirty-three years old, a kind of sensation-rousing holy man who claimed godly lineage.

But he resembled no god that Pretonius knew. To an alert Roman, it was considered safest to stay on the good side of all the gods—Jupiter, Venus, Mars and the rest—all properly worshiped before their temple images. Certainly not out on the wayside, or just anywhere as this fellow was said to have taught. Like most Roman soldiers, Pretonius normally looked to Mithras—the warrior's invincible god of light—as the appropriate god for him.

It was hot and windless as the procession moved out the northwest gate and up the foul slope of Golgotha—"The Place of a Skull"—with its stench of decay, litter of bones and ravens circling overhead. Many had died here on this rocky hill, their bodies cut down and left to the elements.

The crowd milled about on the slope, picking vantage points to watch the proceedings. When some of them ventured too close, Pretonius coldly waved them back.

He stood there grimly, his arms folded, as the soldiers stripped the three prisoners of their clothing, laid them on their backs, their heads on the crossbeams—called *patibula* —and nailed down their outstretched hands. The two bandits screamed and writhed as the nails were driven. The soldiers grunted and cursed, struggling to hold the men's arms in place. But the holy man made no sound of complaint. The long nails were planted, then driven through with sharp strokes of the mallet.

The extended arms of the condemned men were bound to the beams with ropes to support their weight while they were being hoisted. Then, one at a time, the three beams with the bodies affixed to them were raised to the upright stakes. Three soldiers heaved at ropes which ran in grooves over the top to lift each crossbeam with its dangling body. The other soldier climbed upon a stump beside each stake and guided the beam into a notch near the upper end, where it was lashed tightly in place.

The victims' legs were set astride pegs projecting from the uprights, and their feet, positioned so that their knees were slightly bent, were fastened below with nails driven through the instep and sole. Then the arm ropes were removed.

Pretonius dismissed the extra guard, and kept only his execution detail to stay the thing through.

The crowd stared. Time dragged. Pretonius sweated. He loathed the assignment, especially this one, even though crucifixion was a common Roman punishment for non-Roman criminals of the worst sort and slaves. Insurrectionists were the usual culprits. In Syria, he had once watched a mass crucifixion of two thousand rebels. There wasn't enough room for the crosses, and not enough crosses for the bodies. It was the cruelest, most spectacular death known—far worse and more prolonged than stoning, burning, or boiling in oil.

The nails were nothing compared to the muscular agony. It began with the tearing pull of a man's suspended weight, then the slow, vicious cramps curling like knives through the body, the taut flesh constricting the flow of blood. Most of the victims died shrieking maniacs. As they hung by their arms, the knotting of tissues in the torso slowly stifled their breathing, forcing them to raise their weight on the nails in their feet. Then slowly the cords in their legs locked and swelled, bringing them back down. The process repeated itself over and over.

Death came gradually, sometimes taking days, from sheer pain and exhaustion. But the average length of the death throes was about twelve hours. Today the orders were to get it over quickly, before the Passover feast began at nightfall.

Pretonius felt strangely drawn to the imperturbable holy man. He was so incredibly self-possessed, so remote, compared to the other two ranters. The man even refused the draught of opiate wine, mixed with gall, which had been offered him to dull the pain and bring on stupor. He apparently wanted to keep his full senses to the end. The man's chin rested on one shoulder and then the other, his lips moving inaudibly. Pretonius stared up at the *titulus*—the placard—that had been hung around his neck, stating the reasons for his death. In three languages, Hebrew, Latin and Greek, it said: "JESUS OF NAZARETH THE KING OF THE JEWS." Pretonius had heard some of the Sadducean clergy protesting. But Pilate, the governor, had told them, "What I have written I have written."

If this Jesus were a king, he was certainly no king in the common sense, Pretonius thought. Yet he had an air of tragic authority about him. Pretonius rubbed his forehead, his hand unsteady.

Spectators and passers-by on the nearby road jeered at the holy man. "He saved others; let him save himself . . ." Pretonius had an impulse to shout at them for order. But he said nothing. He swallowed dryly.

He thought he detected a note of nervous self-justifi-

cation in some of the outcries. "Thou that destroyest the
temple, and buildest it in three days, save thyself. If thou
be the Son of God, come down from the cross." They
sounded as if they had not been quite sure he wouldn't do
just that. "He saved others; himself he cannot save. If he
be the King of Israel, let him now come down from the
cross, and we will believe him. . . ."

A chill went through Pretonius. He stomped about,
trying to shake off the unsettling impressions.

The soldiers joined in the raillery, then busied themselves dividing the prisoners' belongings. Like jackals,
Pretonius thought. He clamped his jaws. The ghoulish
business was a custom. To the executioners, the spoils!
The soldiers portioned out most of the items, and then
paused over the holy man's seamless cloak.

"Let us not rend it," one said, "but cast lots for it,
whose it shall be." The soldier got out dice, and the four
began their game.

Pretonius eyed them in disgust. Abominable louts!
Frankish and Thracian mercenaries, ignorant Italian volun-
teers! But they would think him gone mad if he stopped
them. He could show no heart. He was a Roman officer,
a centurion, commander of a century, professionally without sentiment, under orders! Carry on!

Pretonius turned his back on them. It was brutal business, particularly in these dreary, malcontent provinces.
No wonder Augustus had stationed this motley Second
Italian Legion out here. Let them do the dirty work. But
if Caesar's procurator says crucify, you crucify. That's
the way the world runs.

Curious, Rome didn't demand such a barbaric fate for its own citizens, no matter how heinous their crimes. The horrible technique had been devised by the Carthaginians, or perhaps the Phoenicians. In any case, the empire soon had picked it up and, along with the Greeks, begun using it as the most frightful penalty ever devised.

Pretonius swatted angrily at the gnats swarming about his ears and wished he were somewhere else, anywhere. He could not escape the obscure feeling that a more monstrous deed than he knew was taking place this day.

The holy man had some indestructible quality in him that reached out insistently. Occasionally his tortured eyes fell on the crowd with a kind of rending pity. Pretonius jerked his sword belt tighter and slapped the strap through the holder. He had to be there. He couldn't have refused. At least he couldn't have stopped it.

Soldiers always had to be there. They had to stand by at these lingering deaths to prevent rescue attempts. It was duty. Pretonius glanced about disconsolately.

He would do what he could. He would see that they didn't break the holy man's legs at the finish, the usual final atrocity in these executions on the cross. It wouldn't be much. But it would be a little. His men already probably thought him gone soft.

Uneasily, Pretonius' gaze stole up to the dying men. They were talking, brokenly, in strained, hoarse voices. Pretonius strove to hear, his nerves jumpy whenever he looked at this man Jesus.

The man was racked with agony, yet it didn't seem to be just for himself alone. He had an unbelievable fortitude, but his suffering seemed even deeper and more crushing because of it.

The two bandits, hard-looking creatures, hung on either side of him. One of them was taunting him, gasping spitefully, "If thou be Christ, save thyself and us." But the other miscreant protested, moaning, "Dost not thou fear God . . . ? . . . we receive the due reward of our deeds: but this man hath done nothing amiss." And he turned miserably toward the holy man, appealing to him, "Lord, remember me . . ."

And this man, this Jesus, with his awesome composure, his almost frightening forbearance, his words still firm with hope despite the pain, the exertion, the tight breathing, said, "Verily . . . I say unto thee, To day shalt thou be . . . with me in paradise."

Pretonius' pulse skipped. It couldn't be so, he told himself furiously. It must be nonsense! What manner of god could he be who asked no burnt offerings, no shrines, no slain oxen laid on an altar; who hung there dying, and asked only one's own belief?

Pretonius paced about distraughtly, scowling, angry at the jeering onlookers, at himself.

After one burst of public derision, the holy man raised his head tremblingly, lifting himself on his feet for air, and implored, "Father, forgive them; for they know not what they do." Tears wet his cheeks. His sweat ran red with blood from the cellular tension, the extreme pain.

A sense of helpless degradation came over Pretonius. "Forgive . . ." How could the man forgive those who killed him? Why? For what? Didn't they know what they were doing? Did he, Pretonius, who carried out this crucifixion, not know what he was doing?

Suddenly the sky began darkening. A strange, cloudless haze thickened over the landscape. All at once a rumble sounded, and the earth shook. A force came racing and split a small fissure in the rocky hill and traveled on across the surface of the ground toward the city.

The soldiers bounded for their weapons and shields, gaping. Screams came from the crowd, and men threw their arms over their heads and ran. Pretonius stood motionless, spellbound.

After that it was very quiet and dark on the hill.

It remained that way for three hours, and Pretonius stood there beside a cross whose shadow covered the earth, and asked himself what the world had done, what each man in it had done, what he had done.

Then the glow of day began creeping back like the dawn. The holy man spoke. "Father, into thy hands I commend my spirit. . . . It is finished." He gave a loud shout—a shout not of defeat but of victory. His body sagged. His head fell forward on his chest. He was dead before the soldiers lanced the three.

It was full light. A bird sang in a carob tree.

Pretonius took off his helmet. "Certainly this was a righteous man," he murmured. He bit his lip, a throbbing at his temples. "Truly this was the Son of God." He knew now. He knew what he had done. He glanced at his men and, ignoring them, dropped to his knees before the cross.

22

MARY

"Now there stood by the cross of Jesus his mother . . ."

MARY LEANED HEAVILY on John's shoulder, her body heaving at moments with deep, racking sobs, as the apostle led her down the rocky slope of Golgotha. She couldn't see or think. She couldn't remember or hope. She could only feel, and die a hundred deaths of her own. Whatever the great purpose her son had served, whatever the reason for his death, whatever the gift to mankind, he was gone, and she had lost her son. To her, in this blackest of moments, that was the one, awful reality.

At the bottom of the hill, she suddenly wrenched about, trying to rush back up the slope, but John held her fast, his arm about her. She hadn't intended to do it, but her body had been prompted by some calling of its own substance, apart from reason.

John kept talking quietly to her, trying to comfort

her, his words not registering clearly, but firm and helpful. He said that everything would be taken care of, that it would be better this way, that a kindly rich man and his servants were preparing the burial, that they would attend to Jesus' body and lay him to rest.

The other women—Mary's sister, Salome; Mary Magdalene; and Mary, the wife of Cleopas—moved along with the tragic pair, they themselves walking blindly, their heads bent forward, veils hiding their faces. They reached the bottom of the hill where some trees grew beside a road, and there John permitted them to stop. Mary had not wanted to come this far, would have stayed up there with her son, but they seemed to think this would be best. John and the others kept repeating that it would be best, that it would be best to let the men attend the burying, that it would be best, best . . . It must be best. She could rest here, though, he said. She could wait here a while and perhaps that would help. Everything that could be done would be done. It didn't matter, though, one way or the other, because Jesus was dead. No matter what they did, he was dead and she could not help him. They could not do anything for him now except bury him, because her son was dead.

Mary straightened up with an effort, one hand still grasping John's arm, attempting to regain her bearing. She shouldn't be a burden on them. It was her own trial to endure, and Jesus would not have her breaking to pieces. She held her head rigidly erect, her lips a tight seam of pain, but the grief kept buckling through her, deep and uncontrollable. John helped her sit down, and the others sat there with her, one of them stroking her hand. Up on the hill, they could see the men working to extract the nails and remove Jesus from the cross. His head hung limply, so that she could see only the crown of his hair.

All through the dark afternoon she had stood up there as near to the cross as the soldiers would let her come, watching her son die, watching him slowly die, her own flesh and blood writhing in pain, her boy slowly, cruelly dying, and there was nothing she could do. What a price to pay, oh Lord, for having such a son.

As she sat huddled there on the grass, the awfulness of it kept surging over her. It would seem to settle down for just a bit, steadying, and then it would burst through her anew, shaking her to the depths of her being, scalding her cheeks and blinding her eyes.

Near the end, when he had known he was about to die, his tormented eyes had sought her out, and she had flung herself toward him, and the others had had to hold her back. Jesus had tried to smile at her, to ease her grief, but all he could manage was a kind of pleading, regretful farewell, as if to say he realized his role had been difficult for her. "... behold thy son!" He had brought her to this, he was saying, he was her son, and she had to bear the anguish of it. Then his pain-clouded eyes had shifted to John, the only one of the apostles there. "Behold thy mother!" She hadn't known quite what he had meant just then, yet in truth she had felt like a mother to all of them, to all of her son's disciples, just as he had said while he was dying, and maybe that was what his words had meant ...

that because he was hers, and they were his, they were hers, too. My son, my son, my dear son . . .

She had tried to conceal the tumult in her as he hung there. She had not wanted her own pain to cause him any more suffering than he already had to bear, if that were possible. But when he had flung his streaked face upward and cried, "My God, my God, why hast thou forsaken me?" she had broken down completely, struggling to reach through to him, and the others had had to restrain her. Then Jesus had exhaled deeply, as if the worst had passed. Mary had fought to calm herself as well. His haggard gaze had shifted about, and he murmured, "I thirst." A soldier put a sponge soaked with vinegar wine on a hyssop stalk and shoved it to his mouth. Then it had all been over.

Mary sat there on the grass, a numbness gradually coming over her body, as if it had worn itself to exhaustion in grief, and only a dry, tight immobility remained. Her mind, her thoughts, seemed to be dissociated from her body, as if she had left it, and it no longer was hers. She knew other people were still about her, yet they seemed to exist only in a vague mist, and she herself wandered apart, in a dim chamber of loss.

". . . for unto whomsoever much is given, of him shall be much required . . ." She had been a maid of about sixteen when he was born, and now she was a widow in her late forties, her husband dead some years ago. All of Jesus' life, she had worried over him, aglow with pride in him, but also troubled—on the flight to Egypt; during moments of youthful independence, as when he slipped off from his parents to talk to the Temple scholars, his long trips into the desert to pray, the gossip about him by the neighbors in Nazareth, their refusal to see how fine, how great he was, their ridicule of his calling, the dangers and criticism that he had met in the course of his work. So often he was away when she wanted him near her; so often, he had to forsake the sheltering warmth of family to labor abroad in the world. After the attack on him in Nazareth, he had stayed mainly at Capernaum. It had been hard for Mary, but she knew he served a greater cause, even as he said that every man must, if necessary in order to serve God, be willing to give up his father, his mother, his wife, children, and brethren and sisters, and his own life also.

At times Mary had felt hurt and left out. A quiet, self-effacing and pious woman, she was not inclined to her son's habit of pricking custom. But she had borne it all, loving him, believing in him. He had mingled with all sorts of questionable people—outcasts, sinners, publicans, lepers, blind men and harlots, with no thought of what people would say or think. But Mary had had unflagging faith in him—that all would turn out for the best. Sometimes, indeed, she and the other women had traveled with him in his preaching. He had always tried, in so far as his responsibilities permitted, to please her, and he had performed his first miracle at her request.

That had been at the little town of Cana, about four miles north of Nazareth, in Jesus' early ministry. Both he and his disciples were there at the house of a friend of Mary's for a wedding. The hosts had run out of wine.

Mary, touched by their embarrassment, had tugged at Jesus' sleeve. "They have no wine," she whispered, impatient for him to do something about it. He chided her gently, "Woman, what have I to do with thee? mine hour is not yet come." Yet Mary, instinctively confident in him, had told the servants, "Whatsoever he saith unto you, do it." Mary knew her son, knew that he would not fail her.

When he found an unobtrusive moment, he told the servants quietly, "Fill the waterpots with water." He always asked others to share in his wonders, even if they could do just a little. They filled the six pots to the brim, each containing eight and three-fourths gallons. Then he told them, "Draw out now, and bear unto the governor of the feast." It was the finest of wine, and the people wondered why the best had been saved until the last. None but Jesus and the servants knew how it had happened. And Mary, on whose appeal he had done it.

He was always so wise and kind and discerning, almost too much so at times for her to comprehend. But never once had she forgotten the secret locked in her heart, that she had been chosen by God to bring Jesus to the world, that she was the channel by which God brought his grace to mankind. Yet she could not know what it all meant, could not understand, not yet, why her son, why God's Son must die, why the world should torture him so, and kill him. They did not know, they did not believe or accept him, and she could not see then why it had to be. ". . . and no man knoweth the Son, but the Father; neither knoweth any man the Father, save the Son, and he to whomsoever the Son will reveal him. . . ."

Up on the hill, Mary could see that they had Jesus' body down now, and were laying it gently on some white sheets. One of them took a basin and cloth, and began washing off the crusted blood and grime. Abruptly, she got to her feet and started back up the slope.

John took her arm again, and this time let her continue back up the hill a way. The men had Jesus' body on a litter and were carrying him down another side of the hill. Mary and the other women and John followed along behind, the women beginning to talk a little more calmly, saying they would prepare spices and bring them tomorrow to anoint Jesus in the tomb.

The litter bearers entered a little garden, well kept and lush with neat beds of flowers and rows of cedars and palms. The tomb was fresh-hewn into the face of a limestone cliff.

At the entrance, Joseph of Arimathea and Nicodemus rubbed Jesus' body with ointments and then wrapped it with strips of linen, pausing as they wound the cloth to spread on reddish-brown resins and other preservatives. Mary watched through a wall of tears, a throbbing in the muscles of her throat.

"He that is faithful in that which is least is faithful also in much . . ." Oh, my son, you were faithful in much, in all, even to death. You will always be with these you left behind, and they will hold to the faith of heaven you brought them . . . your vision, your kingdom. . . .

"The kingdom of heaven is like unto leaven, which a

woman took, and hid in three measures of meal, till the whole was leavened." You are the leaven, my son, in these whom you filled with your love. "It is like a grain of mustard seed, which, when it is sown in the earth, is less than all the seeds that be in the earth: but when it is sown, it groweth up, and becometh greater than all herbs, and shooteth out great branches; so that the fowls of the air may lodge under the shadow of it."

The men lifted Jesus' body and carried it into the dark interior of the tomb. Inexplicably, Mary began to feel her strength coming back to her, only fleetingly at first, a brief sensation, and then after a moment, more fully, flowing through her, and with it a sense of peace.

She had thought for a while she would not be able to go on, with her son dead, with this crushing sorrow on her. She had thought she could not stand it. But she had. All the protective love of motherhood had swelled in her helplessly as he died, and she would gladly have taken his place on the cross. But she couldn't. She had to yield now to her own cross. Jesus had had to suffer for men's sins, to show God cared for them so much he sacrificed his own Son, a ransom for many. Mary could comfort herself, in the fifteen years or more before she died, knowing that she had shared in that sacrifice, in paying that ransom, because she, too, had given her son.

Standing there before the tomb, she turned and looked at John. As Jesus had said, he was like a son to her. All those who had worked at Jesus' side had become like sons, a part of a heavenly family that he had reared to God's glory. He had left her in John's care, and with him she would now make her home.

Her sad gaze turned back to the tomb. The stone wall lay in dusky shadows, but from behind it the westerly sun splashed the brow of the cliff with light. There was a tiny, dark movement on the face of the stone cliff beside the open tomb. It was a beetle, climbing slowly, tirelessly up the sheer wall toward the top. On a night long ago, it had all begun. . . .

Hard though its labors, difficult and arduous though the climb, long though the journey seemed, that humble, struggling life would eventually reach the shining heights.

23

MARY MAGDALENE

"The first day of the week cometh Mary Magdalene . . ."

THE CITY SLEPT. A slender, dark-haired woman hurried through the silent streets, clutching a packet under her arm. Her black garb blended with the night, and in the heavy darkness between the close walls of the buildings, she moved along nearly invisible. But at the junctures of the streets, where the first faint gray of dawn touched the stone pavement, her eyes showed red from sleeplessness and her face lined with sorrow.

Mary Magdalene walked rapidly, looking neither to right nor to left, past the shuttered stalls of the merchants and craftsmen, on toward the edge of the city. A dog barked in the distance, the only sign of life in a bereaved world, and even that sound was far away. Outside the city gate, she could see the three upright stakes on the brow of the hill, one on either side of the cross where he had hung, standing like dark watchmen of doom against the sky. Suddenly the earth seemed to tremble beneath her feet, just for an instant and only slightly. Mary's hands tightened on the packet.

It was the first day of the week, and she carried with her spices—hyssop, rose oil and rose water—to anoint the body of Jesus. She skirted around the foot of the hill along the dirt road; but before she reached the garden, the Temple guards who had been stationed at the tomb to prevent any attempt to remove the body came running out from the trees and hurried off toward the city, breathing hard, their trappings askew, their spears dragging in the dirt. Mary hesitated, then went on. Unless other guards had taken their place, who would be there to roll away the stone for her from the tomb? She followed the path that led into the little garden, curtained with evergreens and shrubbery. Dawn had begun to break, but deep shadows still enveloped the garden. A limb snapped off to one side, and Mary started.

Recovering, she hurried on toward the tomb. When she could make it out, she stopped, breathless. The big stone lay flat on the ground, not rolled away in its groove at all, but tumbled out on its face. The grave gaped dark and silent.

Slowly Mary drew near and peered inside. For a while she could see nothing. Then as her eyes adjusted to the dark interior, her body went rigid. He was not there! She drew back shakily.

Just then the first burst of sunlight flooded the tree-tops.

Mary whirled and ran back through the garden, stumbling over logs and stones. She ran down the sloping path and along the road, her sandals scooping up dust. Through the gate and along the streets of the waking city, she ran, numb to the morning cries of vendors, the drone of the potters' wheels, the sellers of salt with scales, the merchants placing their wares on the racks before their shops. She ran until, reaching the place where Peter and John stayed in adjacent quarters, she called out to them in a frightened voice. "They have taken away the Lord out of the sepulchre," she cried. ". . . we know not where they have laid him."

They started off, the three of them, running again. Mary, already winded, struggled to keep up. Peter's heavy steps pounded on the pavement. Back out through the gate and into the garden they raced, the younger John dashing on ahead. But at the tomb he waited, giving precedence to Peter to enter first.

The entrance was less than the height of a man, and Peter had to stoop to go inside. The new sepulchre had niches hewn in the wall for eight bodies, three on each side and two at the rear. Jesus had been the first to be buried there, and on the slab where he had lain, only the strips of burial linen remained. The napkin that had been placed over his head still stood wrapped over, in an erect, convex position, as if the body had dematerialized without disturbing it.

Mary, pale and tense, stood at the entrance, watching them. Presently they came out, mystified, shaking their heads, at a loss for an explanation. They didn't know what to do. What could they do? Finally they returned to the city. But Mary Magdalene remained, standing alone outside the vacant tomb, weeping. Always in the crucial moments of Jesus' time, it seemed that the women, and often almost no one else, held fast to him. It had been that way at the cross, and it was so again at the bafflingly deserted tomb. Though the men could walk away, Mary Magdalene could not. Her womanly intuition held her at the place where he had lain. She sat down on a rock, and each time the tears dried on her cheeks, new ones came to wash the old away.

During nearly all of Jesus' journeys, from town to town, the women were there, hovering loyally in the background, ministering to him—cooking, listening, sewing, serving. They came from all levels, wives and single women, the wealthy, the poor, the sheltered and the strayed. Mary Magdalene knew keenly how they felt, especially those with bitter pasts. They were bound to him by his gentleness, his words of encouragement and sympathy. Such understanding was little known in those days of harsh judgments and arbitrary condemnation, when a misstep marked a woman forever. But Jesus gave one hope—and a new start. Mary Magdalene, herself a penitent whom Jesus had reclaimed from an unwholesome life, knew the value of such a gift.

According to her name, she came from Magdala, a city at the westernmost reach of the Sea of Galilee, known for its wealth and degeneracy. Dyers and weavers thrived there, and money flowed freely, but the city derived its main reputation from its debauchery. It did big business in turtledoves for purification. A pesthole of tempters and temptresses, it dragged many of its young men and women into the vortex. Robber bands infested its valley approaches, and Rome later destroyed the city because of its depravity.

But Mary Magdalene had escaped the waste and futility she once knew. Jesus, sensitive to her real worth, had freed her from the seven devils of sin that had wrecked her life; he had given her heart where she had known only hurt, had given her happiness and usefulness where before she had known only despair and loss. He had said that those forgiven most love the most, and Mary Magdalene had that kind of love—a great, constant, never-ebbing glow of gratitude for what he had done, for the bright, new hope he had given.

There was that time beside the Temple in Jerusalem, glimmering like a jewel in a life of darkness. The Pharisees, those righteous legalists, had thought they could trap the merciful Jesus. ". . . this woman," they said, flinging their victim toward him, "was taken in adultery, in the very act. Now Moses in the law commanded us, that such should be stoned: but what sayest thou?" The woman had stood there, trembling and terrified. Jesus, his strong countenance troubled and pitying, stooped down to the ground, his forefinger tracing lines in the sand. "He that is without sin among you, let him first cast a stone at her." Slowly, shamefacedly, the accusers turned and walked away, the oldest first and then the younger ones. Jesus was left there alone with her. Tears wet her cheeks, smearing her kohl-painted eyelids. He rose. "Woman," he said gently, "where are those thine accusers? hath no man condemned thee?"

The woman swallowed, trying to speak. "No man, Lord."

"Neither do I condemn thee: go, and sin no more."

It was terrible, beautiful, unforgettable, like a cloud lifting, like chains loosed, like a new life beginning. And it was Jesus' way. "Be ye therefore merciful, as your Father also is merciful. Judge not, and ye shall not be judged: condemn not, and ye shall not be condemned: forgive, and ye shall be forgiven: give, and it shall be given unto you . . ."

Mary Magdalene still held the packet of spices. She unwrapped it, fingering the cruses of oil, the mint-scented powder of the hyssop leaves. She had no use for them now. He was gone. Even his body was gone. Oh Lord, my Lord. . . . Her cheeks burned saltily, and the hot tears came again. Memories drifted over her as she sat there, places and events, and in the midst of all of them, she could see Jesus—working, smiling, kneeling over the sick, talking quietly, encouraging, helping, rejuvenating. The images filed lucidly through her mind, and at moments it almost seemed he lived again. A radiance would creep over her face, and then she would drop back into reality, and there it would be, the dark, cold grave. The catch would return to her throat.

She could not explain why, but she seemed unable to leave the spot. Unreasoningly, her bleak gaze kept returning to the tomb. She knew the uselessness of it, and she forced herself to look elsewhere, out over the evergreens, the lilacs and the white blossoms on the myrtle. The spring leaves appeared motionless, but then as her eyes lingered on them, they seemed to nod and dance.

Mary pressed her hands to her eyes. She refolded the spices and oils in the cloth. Her fingers trembled. She stood up, feeling faint and oddly restive. She looked at the tomb again. It was just the same. She took a few steps toward it and stopped to glance over her shoulder. Then she spun around, staring into the trees. There was nothing, no one.

Why had she turned? She had heard nothing. Yet . . . She apparently had remained here too long alone. In her distraught condition, she could not keep her emotions in check. She should leave. It did no good to stay. But even as she thought thus, she turned back toward the tomb, her legs carrying her toward it. She began crying again, and that, too, seemed almost not a part of her. She bent, looked inside again, and heard herself gasp.

A translucent, shimmering whiteness bathed the slab where Jesus had lain, and two figures, clothed in white, stood at either end. Angels! Mary still stood outside the tomb, and only her head and shoulders leaned into the entrance. She could not move, or speak, and only the sound of another's voice released her. "Woman, why weepest thou?"

"Because," she burst out, "they have taken away my Lord, and I know not where they have laid him."

In that instant, she realized that someone stood behind her. She whirled around and heard the question repeated, "Woman, why weepest thou? whom seekest thou?"

It was the gardener, of course. That was where the voice came from. Her thoughts spinning, she hardly looked at him. Her words tumbled out. "Sir, if thou have borne him hence, tell me where thou hast laid him, and I will take him away."

"Mary." The word came softly, caressing.

Her eyes leaped up to his face then, and her world stood still. "Master!"

It was he. The Lord, risen! Alive again, walking the earth, with his goodness and gentleness and love. Her Savior! Her life regained! She dropped to her knees and reached out to kiss his hand.

"Touch me not," Jesus said gently, "for I am not yet ascended to my Father: but go to my brethren, and say unto them, I ascend unto my Father, and your Father; and to my God, and your God."

Mary went, her feet flying, her heart on wings, knowing that Jesus would never die, that the miracle of his love could not be shut into any grave, that he lived on, walking with her through the darkest paths and deepest sorrows, calling her name in the grimmest gardens; that because she could not bear to give him up, because her own life relied on him and what he stood for, he had come back to her through the mists of death and now lived with her, renewing, steadying, and to stay.

24

MATTHEW

"Then were the disciples glad,
when they saw the Lord."

THEY SAT OR LEANED about the room like dead men. Matthew started to rise, then dropped back down in a corner. The others slumped against the wall or on the floor, their countenances gray and stony. They stirred at times, without reason. They spoke after long silences, without meaning, their voices dry as wind in stubble.

It was all over. The long, high road had plummeted them into the pit. The exalted expedition had ended. The light had gone out. Direction ceased. They were the shards of defeat. They were empty husks, cast on the wayside, set to be trampled into dust.

One of them went over to test the bar on the door. Not that it would provide any protection if the soldiers came with their rams and axes. Not that it mattered greatly if they did come. Jesus was dead; and his disciples were broken men, disillusioned at the fate the Master had met, frightened, and revolted by their own collapse.

Matthew locked his hands in front of his face, his thumbnails clicking against his teeth. It had been quite a downfall, quite a rout. As he and the other tax collectors used to say, the whole bundle had burst.

Matthew's gaze shifted dully about the room. Peter, that unfettered gladiator, sat rubbing his forehead back and forth against his fist, a stricken ruin. Andrew leaned against the wall, his massive arms folded, his face a cloud. John would occasionally take a furious step or two about the floor and raise his hands as if on the verge of a torrent of speech, then drop them, without a word. Nathanael sat motionless, though every so often, a sigh, almost a whimper, came from his lips. Philip kept running his hand through his hair; then he would shake his head in disbelief. The others drooped in their places equally shattered. Thomas was not there.

None of them gave any credence to the feverish reports of Mary Magdalene and some of the other women that angels had told them Jesus had risen from the dead. Mary Magdalene even claimed Jesus himself had appeared to her outside the tomb. Idle tales, all of them. These women let their emotions serve for heads. Neither Matthew nor any of the other apostles believed any of it. Matthew closed his eyes, stroking the bridge of his nose.

Jesus had died, defenseless against the rulers. He had died as an ordinary mortal would die, and in the most horrible manner possible. After all his inspiring teachings about "life eternal," he had been cut down, bestially. He had warned them there would be persecutions, but that they could surmount any obstacle. Yet he himself had been destroyed. And they had run like ferrets to their holes. Matthew felt raw and denuded, stripped to the marrow, his mind ripped bare.

He took a long, despondent breath. What now? The bright cloud was scattered. The world was turned to rust. To the right, whirlwinds. To the left, desolation. Forward, blindness. Backward, a void.

He used to be quite a figure, harnessed to Rome for its pelf. He made money, all right, levying customs at his toll station in Capernaum. It was a sure-paying location, there on the trade route between Ptolemais and Damascus, catching the maritime commerce across the lake with the pagan cities of the Decapolis. He had been only a collector, a *portitore,* under the regional customs supervisors, the publicans, but he had received a handsome share all the same—enough to live in lush style. He never had been able to reconcile himself to it, though, and his dissatisfaction had stemmed from more than being ostracized by fellow Jews as a sycophant of Rome. It wasn't just that, alone. He had plenty of confreres, a fast social circle among the godless. But his expansive nature and intellect had champed at the narrowness of his life. A gregarious man of charm and education, versed in Greek and Hebrew, endowed with literary gifts, he had been miserable and stultified in the company of shady money, stunted minds, chicanery, dowdy conversation and jaded sensibilities. His name had been Levi, then, a brother to vultures, a companion to owls. When Jesus came along, life to Matthew spread out like a green, fertile field. "Follow me," Jesus said. And Matthew did.

In gratitude and celebration, he had given a dinner, and even though his only other guests had been necessarily his old associates, Jesus had come graciously, despite criticism from the religious readers. ". . . I will have mercy . . ." he had said.

Being accepted by Jesus marked a transformation in Matthew. Until then, he had been unable to break free. He had been trapped, arbitrarily classified and branded by his profession. A tax gatherer's money, even, was refused for alms. His word wasn't good in a Jewish court. But Jesus had given him a chance, welcomed him, drawn him out of the old mire, and made the new Matthew.

Jesus had given him that name, "Mattija" or Matthew, "the gift of Jehovah." Ah, what towering vision the Master possessed, what a closely discerning eye, what harmonies of wit and compassion. What entrancing stories he could tell, pungent with relevance. Matthew, who loved the fine turn of phrase and meaning, would never forget them. The Master could invest the smallest incident, the most common activity, with illuminating significance, and do it with either gentle whimsy or deflating impact. Time after time, he would weave those little stories, scores of them, those parables of farmers, lawyers, noblemen, servants, bridesmaids, birds, lamps, the revelers and the mild, serpents, shepherds, candles, sheep, seeds, soil, trees and wind, each one a gem of living truth. Matthew had jotted down some of them along the way.

He fished in the pocket of his girdle now and drew

out the worn little scroll, untied it and let his eyes wander over the hurried notes . . . a wise man built his house on a rock, ". . . and the rain descended, and the floods came, and the winds blew, and beat upon that house; and it fell not: for it was founded upon a rock." But not so, the foolish man's house. It was built on sand, ". . . and great was the fall of it."

Matthew twisted the scroll tightly and put it away. It did no good to mull over the remnants. Their own hopes had come tumbling down, like a house built on sand. And now they groped as if they had no eyes, like the blind against a wall, huddled here in this garret, morose, disappointed, disgusted with themselves, afraid. They might as well have been buried with Jesus.

A rapid, restrained knocking sounded against the door, and they all started. Matthew got to his feet. Peter, pulling himself together, strode over, lifted the bar and grimly flung the door wide, as if inviting the worst. But it was only two followers, Cleopas and another. They both began talking at once, their faces flushed, bobbing their heads at each other's words. The apostles regarded them dourly.

As best Matthew could make out, the pair had been walking along the road winding west from Jerusalem toward Emmaus, when a stranger joined them and lectured them about the Scriptures. They had induced the stranger to stop with them at an inn, and, as they broke bread, they had suddenly realized that the stranger was Jesus. At that moment, he vanished. They claimed they hadn't recognized him at first because he appeared "in another form," but in the end, their eyes were opened.

More hallucinations. Matthew propped his shoulder against the wall. These wishful fantasies only scraped the sore deeper, but it was no use arguing with the bearers of them. It was pitiable, actually, the way these two men wanted Jesus to live so badly they imagined he did. This gibberish about walking with a man four miles before they recognized him—even the women had done better than that.

Peter closed the door again and barred it. The two visitors sputtered a little more, overwrought. But they got nowhere and, under the bitter gaze of the apostles, they gradually became silent. But their rabid talk, the friction of views, left the mood of the gathering even more strained than before. This loose talebearing could provoke further reprisals, although that could hardly increase the already total debacle. They could merely lose their own lives. Matthew knew that the priests had bribed the Temple guards to claim that the apostles had stolen Jesus' body from the tomb. It apparently was a scheme to convict and wipe out the remaining leaders of the movement—himself, these other hulls of men, who had lost their cause and their self-respect and now might die in their disgrace.

Nathanael, sitting on the floor, had been flopping his sandaled foot rhythmically against the stone. Slap, slap, slap. Now he stopped. A sudden silence drew around them. Simultaneously, they all became strangely immobile, like fixed, inanimate objects. The silence stretched out interminably. Matthew could feel the ugly, raw knowledge of their own conduct, of their shabby plight, drawing tighter around them. It seemed as if a strangling vise closed about the room. This was a grave, and the walls were shrinking inward. Matthew could hardly breathe. Then a wave as of hot fluid shot through his veins, and he stood up straight, his senses rapier-sharp.

Not a movement had been made. The door had remained closed. There had been no sound. The dusky light in the room was still the same. But there in the middle of the room stood Jesus. "Peace be unto you," he said. Matthew couldn't budge, but a new heart grew where his old one had been.

"Peace be unto you," Jesus said again. "Why are ye troubled? . . . it is I myself." His kindly eyes turned about the room, pausing on each of them in proud affection. ". . . as my Father hath sent me, even so send I you." He spread his hands, and a warm, gentle movement of air enveloped them, caressing them, penetrating them like the soft rays of morning sun. "Receive ye the Holy Ghost," Jesus said. "Whose soever sins ye remit, they are remitted unto them; and whose soever sins ye retain, they are retained."

Then he was gone.

Matthew stood there a moment, a blissful new power pervading him, and then he dropped to his knees, crying like a child, blurting happy, disjointed praises, lifted up on an ocean of gladness. The others were shouting, clapping their hands, crying, making joyful exclamations, singing mingled words of glory to Jesus, the Lord, their risen Master. Then they were all turning to each other, shaking their heads in wonderment, tears of happiness on their faces, embracing each other and giving thanks.

Their world was reborn.

"I am the resurrection, and the life: he that believeth in me, though he were dead, yet shall he live . . ."

It was as if they themselves had descended into the blackest gulf with Jesus, had been humbled and smitten and crushed to the very core, had felt his cross even as he said they must, and that now with him, they had come back to the bright and brimming fullness, not only of the life their bodies contained, but of a life that ascended ever higher, into clearer knowledge and surer faith, into a vast and splendid universe that they never before had known existed, where Jesus stood with them, majestic, loving, just, omnipotent over all time and place.

The apostles would never be afraid again.

They saw him again, eight days later, in that same room. Perhaps he came because of Thomas. Like the others, Thomas could not accept a secondhand account. "Except I shall see in his hands the print of the nails, and put my finger into the print of the nails, and thrust my hand into his side," he said, "I will not believe."

So Jesus came to them again, telling Thomas:

"Reach hither thy finger, and behold my hands; and reach hither thy hand, and thrust it into my side: and be not faithless, but believing."

Beloved old Thomas made no move to carry out his crude inspection. He needed no more than the others to be convinced. The sight alone of the transfigured Christ banished all doubt and melted his heart. His sad eyes filled, and he affirmed stoutly, "My Lord and my God."

"Thomas," Jesus said, and he could have been talking to all of them, to everyone, "because thou hast seen me, thou hast believed: blessed are they that have not seen, and yet have believed."

Then he was gone once more.

Seven of them saw him later on the seashore, but to Matthew, the most memorable occasion would occur forty days after the Resurrection, on a mountain in Galilee. Already Matthew had realized that Jesus must return into the overarching nature of God. He had said so many times, but in the past they had been unable to conceive of it.

All of Jesus' teachings, once hard to grasp, now began to come clear, to shape into a single magnificent design, its sublimity dwarfing into nothingness the petty, literal notions the apostles once had held. It was as if he had imbued them now with something of his own ways and mind, so that they could rise above themselves in understanding, energy and courage.

He had shaken them to the quick, and in his newness they became new. They were transformed men, weak mortals turned into giants, the clouds of confusion turned into pure, straight shafts of light, knowing now that God had shown his face to the world in Jesus and thereby written in plain and human language the way unto himself, that Jesus would build no paltry manlike kingdom, but reigned in a higher sphere, over all and in all, his essence, his love residing, stronger than mountains and swords, within reach

of every man. His life on earth had been itself the greatest parable of them all.

Matthew got out his old notes, studying them, remembering, every word and act now assuming new im-
portance and clarity. "And this gospel of the kingdom
shall be preached in all the world for a witness unto all
nations; and then shall the end come. . . . as the lightning
cometh out of the east . . ."

It would take much time and much work to preach
the gospel to all the nations, but Matthew and the others
would make the difficult beginning, fearless now, undeviating, knowing that in the end ". . . they shall come from
the east, and from the west, and from the north, and from
the south, and shall sit down in the kingdom of God."
Matthew himself carried the message into the region south
of the Caspian Sea, into Macedonia, Persia and Syria. Leg-
end says he was burned to death or beheaded, martyred
like the rest of Jesus' apostles for publishing a story still
unfolding—the immortal book of life. Matthew, in his
record that would stand through the ages, told of that
last scene on the mountain where five hundred people
were assembled, some of them doubting as they always
would, and the eleven apostles were there, before Jesus
ascended into the entity of God. "And Jesus came and
spake unto them, saying, All power is given unto me in
heaven and in earth. Go ye therefore, and teach all nations, baptizing them in the name of the Father, and of the
Son, and of the Holy Ghost: teaching them to observe all
things whatsoever I have commanded you: and, lo, I am
with you alway, even unto the end of the world."

EPILOGUE

PAUL AND
THE GREAT LESSON

*". . . old things are passed away; behold,
all things are become new."*

THE SCALES FELL from his eyes and he could see. He could see for the first time. He could see the deep and cataclysmic secret of life laid bare in one being: Jesus.

He stirred on the bamboo mattress, gazing about weakly at the strange room. It was like awakening in another world. He was shorn of all his dogmatic conceits, left exposed and supplicant. "O wretched man that I am!"

Astounding that these chastened words should ever be wrenched from one who had been so proud, so positive, so self-righteous that he made himself an arbiter for God. Yet that was the phenomenon of Paul, and it contained a discovery for humanity. He epitomized, in striking manner, a universal problem and the answer found in Jesus.

It was to Paul that Jesus made a singular appearance

on earth. ". . . last of all he was seen of me," the apostle later related, ". . . as of one born out of due time." Before it happened, Paul had tried to batter the name of Jesus into extinction.

He was a young scholar of tempestuous force. Brilliant, iron-willed, tireless, he had studied in his native city of Tarsus, a center of world learning; and sat at the feet of the great rabbi, Gamaliel, in Jerusalem. Both Jew and Roman citizen, he used then his Hebrew name, Saul, instead of his Latin name, Paul. Atop his small body perched a large, wide-browed head. He was both selfless and domineering; both adamant and compassionate. He was a mixture, a conflict, a volcanic blend of human striving for perfection. It was this that drove him, lashed him, and hurled him against the wall of man's true nature. He made himself both judge and avenger. With a band of fanatic subordinates, he roamed the Holy City, seeking out the heretics who believed in Jesus, threatening the disciples, casting their followers into prison, having them flogged, letting one of them, Stephen, be stoned to death.

All of the persecution, he did in the name of righteousness, pitying the victims even as he punished them, pleading with them to abandon what he considered a dangerous misconception, a false Messiah, a crucified despoiler of the Torah. Saul knew well the depravity that prevailed everywhere outside the little preserve of Judaism, and he fought against any deviation, any leniency in its prescribed disciplines. But his methods seared his conscience. He shuddered at the obstinacy of the followers of Jesus, the way they forgave him even as his men laid stripes on them.

"Lord Jesus . . ." Stephen had cried, as his body crumpled bloody among the stones, ". . . lay not this sin to their charge."

Saul got so he could no longer sleep. At times on his rounds a dizziness would seize him and he would fall to the ground in convulsions. His friends turned against him. His teacher, the honored Pharisee, Gamaliel, repudiated him. Saul, tortured in his isolation, felt compelled to quit Jerusalem.

Since belief in Jesus was spreading to synagogues in other countries, he obtained from the high priest authority to go to Damascus and arrest followers there. A detachment of Temple guards accompanied him. So did the demons of uncertainty.

Saul and the guards tramped across country, sleeping in the open to avoid pollution and the unclean foods at the inns of Gentile idolators. Finally they wound down from the heights around Mount Hermon into the lowlands approaching Damascus. The sun turned the flat plain into a caldron, the heat rippling like white flames across the sand. Saul's body labored against the heat, and his mind against a storm of doubts. All his zeal for holiness convinced him that the ancient Mosaic laws and traditions provided the only definitive standards of virtue. He knew Jesus had not renounced the law, but had maintained that he represented a higher plane of goodness, where the intents of the heart counted for more than ritual conformity. And he had portrayed his own death as atonement for the inevitable shortcomings of men—extending pardon to all who sought it as fallible, dependent children.

All this to Saul seemed to diminish the law as the ultimate test of purity. How else judge a man except by outward compliance to defined practices? How read the heart? Saul himself adhered rigorously to every rule and precept. Did that not make him truly godly? He bridled at any weakness. He was righteous, devout, pure. But he could still hear Stephen's cries.

The sunlight gave the air a metallic glaze, as if the earth itself had turned into a molten sun. Or else the earth had risen until its surface skimmed those upper fires. A lassitude crept up Saul's legs, stole over his body, and a million bright needles streamed toward his eyes. He seemed to be walking on a high, narrow ledge, far up toward the sun, with sheer walls dropping on either side into a bottomless void. He had to be right—he wielded an arm for God! He stumbled dizzily. Fiery streamers laced the heavens. A huge, blinding light rushed toward him. He was falling, falling, falling, enmeshed in folds of stinging, prickling guilt. He had betrayed God! He had committed crimes against man! He who proclaimed himself most righteous was most evil! He was falling, falling into perdition, smothered in guilt.

Face down in the dirt, he heard a voice appealing to him. "Saul, Saul, why persecutest thou me?"

Saul lay crushed, weak, unable to see. He groaned in the dirt. "Who art thou, Lord?"

"I am Jesus whom thou persecutest: it is hard for thee to kick against the pricks."

Saul trembled, and his voice came feebly, like that

of a fallible, dependent child. "Lord, what wilt thou have me to do?"

". . . rise, and stand upon thy feet: for I have appeared unto thee for this purpose, to make thee a minister and a witness [to] the Gentiles, unto whom now I send thee, to open their eyes, and to turn them from darkness to light . . ."

That is how Saul came to know Jesus. The shock left him blind, and prostrate with remorse. The guards carried him to a house in Damascus, where a follower of Jesus, Ananias, came to care for him, feed him warm gruels, and anoint his eyes. Three days went by before the crust slid from his eyes, and he could see. And then it was as if he could see for the first time—see himself and mankind and glimpse God's tremendous design for his children of the earth.

It did not come to him all at once. Neither he nor any other man has ever comprehended it entirely. But from his own experience, out of the vain presumptions that had only led him into moral catastrophe, Paul had learned a basic truth about man: ". . . evil is present with me. . . . I delight in the law of God . . . but I see another law in my members, warring against the law of my mind, and bringing me into captivity to the law of sin . . ."

Many years would elapse before he put these words down in his letters, but it was that shattering metamorphosis at Damascus that first revealed to him the naked fact of man's dilemma: ". . . the good that I would I do not: but the evil which I would not, that I do. . . ."

That weakness, that terrible failure, had stained the

pages of the past for Paul, for all men, for all nations, ever since Adam in his vanity had sought to make himself supreme; and it would go on distorting and thwarting men, those creatures endowed with the soul of God, with a free will of their own who had chosen their own course, who had through ages past sown the seeds of selfishness and hatred in the world that God had given them, who were now the victims of the influences that they themselves had reared up in their midst, a heritage that ensnared them in arrogant delusions, entangled them in bigotry, injuries and neglect, that trapped them in moral cul-de-sacs. By themselves, they could not escape; they were helpless before the monsters of their own creation.

This was the realization which had prostrated Paul. ". . . for all have sinned, and come short of the glory of God . . ."

What could be done? What was the answer? From the germinal spark within them, men still reached out desperately for their highest fulfillment—for God. But how could they attain it now that they had fouled their native element?

Paul, stripped of his own self-deceits, laid low and raw as an infant before his Maker, sought the solution in Jesus.

After his recovery, he hid himself for months in the desert, repenting. Eventually he returned to Jerusalem, there steeped himself in the teachings of Jesus, listened to the apostles. The ancient law and the prophets had pointed to a coming redeemer, all of which Paul knew thoroughly. He could recognize now who Jesus was, what he stood for, why he had come and what he had done. Paul set out to tell the world about it. His zeal for the cause became limitless, his sense of closeness to Jesus so great, his assurance that he knew him so strong, that Paul often received counsel from him.

Through the years, he journeyed to the callous, oppressive cities of pagan Asia and Europe, spreading the compassion of Jesus, explaining the wondrous legacy he had left to mankind, the secret of life he had revealed, the riddle of humanity he had unraveled. Its scope could hardly be told in man's words.

Paul would try, but first he took another far-reaching step. He who had railed against Jesus for weakening the ancestral codes of diet, circumcision and ceremony became the chief advocate for a relaxation of those rules in respect to the Gentiles, so as to bring them more readily into the congregations of believers. In a crucial council of the apostles on this issue, the largehearted Peter supported Paul's proposal, recalling Jesus' instructions concerning the Gentiles: ". . . God, which knoweth the hearts . . . put no difference between us and them, purifying their hearts by faith." All the regulations, Peter said, would be an unnecessary barrier. Thus, with the backing of Peter, the head of the apostles, and finally with the support of the others, Paul was commissioned to accept Gentiles without binding them to the old laws of diet, circumcision and other conventions. The issue arose repeatedly, sometimes splitting congregations, but it opened a door which had been kept shut for ages.

Paul himself scrupulously observed the Jewish laws of food and purity. ". . . I am a Pharisee, the son of a

Pharisee . . ." Nevertheless, he cleared away the obstacles so that others might enter the broad, rich pastures of Jesus. "There is neither Jew nor Greek, there is neither bond nor free, there is neither male nor female: for ye are all one in Christ Jesus. . . ."

In his ceaseless travels Paul worked mainly through the Jewish synagogues in each foreign city, implanting the knowledge of Jesus, then drawing Gentiles into the congregation. This was the pattern through most of his career. The synagogue was the cradle of the church. It was the only place where God was known. It was about the only place where compassion for fellow men was cultivated. Such an emotion was mostly alien to paganism.

Paul took with him devoted helpers, sometimes his lifelong friend, Bar-Nabas, and John Mark, sometimes Titus and young Timothy, newly won recruits, sometimes others. In his journeys he kept up his trade as a tentmaker, his road-sore feet still skillful on the treadle, his wiry hands flicking the spools and beam. And from place to place, he wrote or dictated letters, dispatching them by travelers to be read in the congregations he or others had founded in Corinth, Thessalonica, Philippi, Ephesus, Rome and elsewhere, encouraging them, guiding them, stressing the mighty work that Jesus had wrought to bring the lost human family back within reach of its Creator.

". . . God was in Christ, reconciling the world unto himself . . ." Paul wrote. That was the great and awesome gift of Jesus. ". . . God commendeth his love toward us, in that, while we were yet sinners, Christ died for us. . . ."

As Jesus had said, he and God were the same, and he had come in the form of man, out of love for men, to take upon himself the penalty for their mistakes, to face for them the inexorable justice of God, to purchase a pardon for all who accepted him.

". . . no man cometh unto the Father, but by me," Jesus had said. . . . "I am the good shepherd: the good shepherd giveth his life for the sheep. . . . I am the door: by me if any man enter in, he shall be saved . . . He that believeth on the Son hath everlasting life . . ."

He had bridged the gulf between man and God. He had extended the ladder of Jacob's dream from the pinnacle of the Almighty to the lowest descent of man. ". . . we were reconciled to God by the death of his Son, much more . . . we shall be saved by his life," Paul wrote. ". . . we are the children of God: and if children, then heirs; heirs of God, and joint-heirs with Christ . . ."

It was an unfathomable mystery, beyond the narrow compass of man, working through the infinite, unshakable laws of balance in all creation, whereby God's own suffering through his son counterweighed the punishment men had earned, and brought forgiveness for all who accept it, have faith in it, and are willing to share it by their own sacrifices in Christ's behalf. Man's circumscribed mind could never grasp it fully, for man could never fully explain even the functions of his own nature and the forces about him, but it was the majestic truth proclaimed through all the words, acts, the death and resurrection of Jesus.

Somehow, in that moment when Jesus hung on the

cross, when the evil and pain of the world fell on him alone and he cried, "My God, my God, why hast thou forsaken me?", there in that instant of hell, of banishment from God, Jesus gave what he had promised: "a ransom for many." And whosoever will offer ". . . his life for my sake and the gospel's, the same shall save it. . . . I am the resurrection, and the life: he that believeth in me, though he were dead, yet shall he live . . ."

How could mere man ever grasp what happened there when Christ hung between heaven and earth? How could man, who lives but a moment in time and knows not even what lies beyond the stars, ever calculate the eternal verities of God, who occupies all space, who has no beginning and no end?

We cannot, Paul knew. We are like children who think and speak as children, but one day we will put away childish things, and understand with mature intelligence. "For now we see through a glass, darkly; but then face to face . . ."

It was faith, knowledge beyond the known, that marked the way to God through the grace of Christ. "Now faith is the substance of things hoped for, the evidence of things not seen. . . ."

Paul, in his ceaseless travels and his work in the heathen cities, often went hungry, was stoned, imprisoned, beaten, robbed, shipwrecked, and finally sent under arrest to Rome, surviving another shipwreck on the way.

"What shall we then say to these things? If God be for us, who can be against us? . . . Who shall separate us from the love of Christ? shall tribulation, or distress, or

persecution, or famine, or nakedness, or peril, or sword?
. . . Nay, in all these things we are more than conquerors
through him that loved us."

Not only had Jesus given humanity a fresh chance,
but he had unmasked the great mystery. He had disclosed
what God is like. He was God, become man, so that man
could know God better. ". . . he that hath seen me hath
seen the Father . . ."

In this, too, Paul realized, Jesus had untangled a
labyrinthine puzzle of the soul. From ages past, Judaism
had recognized that men were God's children—created
spiritually in "his own image." But what was this image?
The answer came in Jesus, ". . . the image of the invisible
God . . ."

He came as a living, tangible manifestation of the
divinity that all men share—a quality to be enlarged or
diminished within themselves. Before he came, men had
felt that they didn't know exactly what that godly element
was in human form, or how to go about nurturing it, or
what pitfalls might limit it—until he showed them God in
flesh and word and deed. He offered, Paul said, ". . . an
example, that ye should follow his steps . . ."

Before Jesus departed from the earth, he said God will
"give you another Comforter [the Holy Ghost], that he
may abide with you for ever, *even* the Spirit of truth." In
declaring these various aspects of God, he displayed a mystic diffusion called the Trinity—God, his incarnation as
man, his all-enveloping spirit, all united—"and these three
are one."

But Paul saw that it was in Jesus who came "in the

likeness of man . . . in fashion as a man"—one both wholly man and wholly God—that the world received the lamp unto its feet. He gave man a clearer view, an earthly demonstration, of just what constituted God on this earthbound plane and laid the goal before men to guide them on their course. What did he do, or say, to provide such revelation?

He was a plain-talking, sympathetic, forthright man who liked flowers and fields and livestock, who held youngsters on his knee, who considered every person, rich or poor, learned or simple, male or female, of the same priceless worth. His message was that all men are related to God, free to husband that divine part of themselves as they choose in seeking fulfillment, and he described the ultimate potentiality: "That they all may be one; as thou, Father, *art* in me, and I in thee, that they also may be one in us . . ."

But Jesus didn't shut himself off in some ethereal realm during his earthly sojourn. He plunged into the world itself, a walking, breathing definition of forgiveness, kindness, understanding and gentleness; a living condemnation of hypocrisy, of pompous technicalities that have nothing to do with justice, of greed and the pursuit of shallow material objectives. He was a man of action who put even his teachings in the form of concrete events, parables about sowers, strayed sheep, rich men, rulers, wayfarers, foreigners, families, foxes, laborers and builders. He came to the world to be in it, not apart. But he wrought his revolutions in the heart, not with armies or institutions.

He attended weddings and rich men's banquets, and he also associated with the sick, dishonored and rejected. He mourned with the sorrowing, was glad with the rejoicing. He noticed the smallest, most common thing on this planet—a mother hen gathering her chicks, the wind blowing where it wills, the weeds in wheat, yeast working in dough, the cunning of a serpent, the beauty of lilies and the chirping of a sparrow. But the kernel of all he did and said was in one word: *love*. "Thou shalt love the Lord thy God with all thy heart, and with all thy soul, and with all thy mind. . . ." and "thy neighbour as thyself." That is what God was like during his visit to earth. He came here out of love to help men find their way, and that is what he was while here—the embodiment of love.

And this was the message that Paul declared, far and wide. Though you may speak with the tongue of men and angels, he said, and have not love, you are become "as sounding brass, or a tinkling cymbal." Though you may understand all mysteries and all knowledge and have all faith so that you could remove mountains and have not love, you are nothing. Though the truths of Jesus might baffle all men's wisdom, his way was straight and simple.

For more then thirty years Paul spread that faith across the known world. Finally, in the great persecutions in Rome under Nero, he was beheaded. But Paul, who once sought to seal God's word within narrow walls, who once fought to bar the gates, had flung them wide to the world. Paul, who once thought himself most right only to find he was most wrong, had found release from the universal plague of sin, and gained new life in Jesus.

"Now therefore ye are no more strangers and foreigners, but fellow-citizens with the saints, and of the household of God . . ."

Jesus had spanned the gap of loneliness separating men from their God. He had marked the hidden trail by which lost sheep could find the fold. But even so, he didn't expect men to understand it all, or all of what he is, or what they are, or can become. As Paul said:

". . . now we see not yet all things . . . But we see Jesus . . ."

AUTHOR'S NOTE

THE CENTRAL EVENTS, places and people of these stories are from the Scriptures. Supplementary background and appropriate emotional atmosphere have been added to round them out. All of the quoted dialogue, except minor instances in the accounts of Herod the Great and the centurion, Pretonius, is taken verbatim from the King James version of the Bible, whose example has also been followed in the main text in respect to the non-capitalization of pronouns referring to Jesus. The name Pretonius is derived from tradition, not recorded history; some early church writers give his name as Longinus. In the chapters on persons participating in the early phases of Jesus' life, some details are included which are not fully substantiated, but which are implied by the scant facts available and by the customs and settings of the times. Simeon's status as a teacher is conjectural, but supported by tradition. Salome's relationship to Jesus' mother, Mary, is not specifically set forth in the Bible, but the fact that in different gospel descriptions of an incident, one lists Salome and another substitutes "his mother's sister" without naming her, provides grounds for assuming she was Mary's close kin. That they traveled together to Jerusalem is indicated by the fact that Jesus' family was in a large party, and relatives in the same region went up to the festivals en masse. Theories differ on Joses' relationship to Jesus. Most church authorities hold that he and others were cousins, called brothers by custom in those days; some believe he was a son of Joseph by a previous marriage, and some consider him a full brother.

Some of these accounts, in briefer form, were written originally for the Associated Press, to whom my publisher, William Morrow and Co., Inc., and I are indebted for permission to develop that material into this more extensive effort to portray Jesus through the eyes of his contemporaries.

GEORGE W. CORNELL

New York, N.Y.
June 1, 1957

SELECTED BIBLIOGRAPHY

BUTLER, ALBAN. *Lives of the Saints*. Revised and supplemented by HERBERT THURSTON, S.J., and DONALD ATTWATER. 4 vols. New York: P. J. Kenedy & Sons, 1956.

CRAIG, CLARENCE TUCKER. *The Beginning of Christianity*. Nashville: Abingdon-Cokesbury Press, 1943.

DAVENPORT, MILLIA. *The Book of Costume*. 2 vols. New York: Crown Publishers, Inc., 1948.

EDERSHEIM, ALFRED. *The Life and Times of Jesus the Messiah*. 2 vols. London: Longmans, Green & Co., Ltd., 1950.

ENSLIN, MORTON SCOTT. *Christian Beginnings*. New York: Harper & Brothers, 1938.

GOGUEL, MAURICE. *The Life of Jesus*. Translated by OLIVE WYON. The Macmillan Co., 1944.

HARMON, NOLAN B. (ed.). *The Interpreter's Bible*. 12 vols. Nashville: Abingdon-Cokesbury Press, 1951.

HASTINGS, JAMES, and others (eds.). *Dictionary of the Bible*. New York: Charles Scribner's Sons, 1954.

HEADLAM, ARTHUR C. *The Life and Teaching of Jesus the Christ*. London: John Murray Ltd., 1936.

HOLTZMANN, OSCAR. *The Life of Jesus*. Translated by J. T.

BEALBY and MAURICE A. CANNEY. London: A. & C. Black, 1904.

HOUSTON, MARY G. *Ancient Egyptian, Mesopotamian and Persian Costume and Decoration.* New York: The Macmillan Co., 1954.

KLAUSNER, JOSEPH. *Jesus of Nazareth.* Translated by HERBERT DANBY. New York: The Macmillan Co., 1929.

LANDMAN, ISAAC, and RITTENBERG, LOUIS (eds.). *Universal Jewish Encyclopedia.* 10 vols. Brooklyn: Universal Jewish Encyclopedia, Inc., 1939-1943.

MACKINNON, JAMES. *The Historic Jesus.* London: Longmans, Green and Co., Ltd., 1931.

MILLER, MADELEINE S., and J. L. *Encyclopaedia of Bible Life.* New York: Harper & Brothers, 1944.

ORR, JAMES (ed.). *The International Standard Bible Encyclopaedia.* 8 vols. Revised edition ed. by MELVIN GROVE KYLE. Grand Rapids: Wm. B. Eerdmans Publishing Co., 1949.

PACE, EDWARD A., and others (eds.). *The Catholic Encyclopedia.* New York: The Gilmary Society, Inc., 1936.

SMITH, SIR GEORGE ADAM. *Jerusalem.* 2 vols. London: Hodder and Stoughton, 1907.

SMITH, J. M. POWIS. *The Prophets and Their Times.* Revised edition. Chicago: The University of Chicago Press, 1941.

SMITH, WILLIAM, and WACE, HENRY (eds.). *Dictionary of Christian Biography.* 4 vols. London: John Murray Ltd., 1880.

STEVENS, WILLIAM ARNOLD, and BURTON, ERNEST DE WITT. *A Harmony of the Gospels.* New York: Charles Scribner's Sons, 1904.